CONTENTS

© 1982 HBJ

CHAPTER ONE

The Parts of Speech

We need words in order to talk about the things we know, the things we study. We also need a special set of words in order to study and talk about our language, so that we can learn to speak and write it more effectively. Some of these special language words are called *parts of speech*. There are only eight of them. They name the eight ways in which words can be used in English. In this chapter we shall study these eight parts of speech.

LESSON 1

Nouns

Nouns are the naming words of language. Notice the words printed in red in the following examples.

EXAMPLES   Barbara Jordan walked onto the platform.
               That car needs a headlight.

A noun is a word used to name a person, place, thing, or idea.

Words like the following (and like those printed in red in the examples) are all nouns.

PERSONS   Barbara Jordan, cousin, teacher, president
PLACES   platform, city, Tulsa, state, New Mexico
THINGS   car, cushion, snail, animal, headlight
IDEAS   intelligence, depth, strength, beauty

Notice that a few of these nouns begin with capital letters. A noun that begins with a capital letter is called a *proper noun*. A proper noun names a particular person, place, or thing. A *common noun*, on the other hand, does not name a particular person, place, or thing.

PROPER NOUNS	COMMON NOUNS
Margaret Thatcher	woman, prime minister
Florida, the Pentagon	state, building
Harcourt Brace Jovanovich	business, organization, corporation

EXERCISE A There are twenty-five nouns in the following paragraph. Draw a line under all of the nouns. (The word *he* is *not* a noun.) Notice the first sentence, which is done for you. (Add 4 points for each correct answer.)

THOMAS EDISON

1   Perhaps the most surprising thing about the inventor Thomas Edison

2   was that he never seemed to need any sleep. Most people need eight

3   to ten hours of sleep each night. Edison, however, was able to sleep

4   much less and still work efficiently. As a young man he began the

5   schedule he continued all his life. During the day he earned his living.

6   At night he read and studied, filling huge notebooks with notes on the

7   books he read and the experiments he made. He rarely slept more than

8   four hours out of twenty-four. He had great powers of concentration.

9   When he was working on a project, he might go for days with hardly

10   any rest. His definition of genius was, "Two percent inspiration and 98

11   percent perspiration."

EXERCISE B Underline all the common nouns in the following sentences. Write in a capital letter for any proper nouns that you find. The capital letters for the proper nouns have been left out on purpose, but remember that ordinarily a proper noun must be capitalized. A proper noun made up of more than one word still counts as just one noun. (Add 10 points for each correctly marked sentence.)

A. This river flows into the atlantic ocean.

1. Elephants live in both africa and india.

2. The prize for peace went to sister theresa.

3. Last week margaret left for a new job in japan.

4. The team won a gold medal in hockey at the olympic games.

5. The dark-haired girl is an exchange student from colombia.

6. To play baseball, ellen needs a mitt and some spiked shoes.

7. Some new records are what debbie wants for her birthday.

8. Armand wants to be a chef like his brother.

9. The fox river flows into lake michigan at green bay.

10. Our family visited the world trade center in new york city.

2

Pronouns

We would probably never write or say a sentence like this one:

Estelle wondered if *Estelle* should invite *Estelle's* brother to the party.

The name *Estelle* occurs too many times in this sentence. To avoid tiresome repetition, we would say something like this:

Estelle wondered if **she** should invite **her** brother to the party.

The words printed in red are pronouns. *She* has replaced *Estelle,* and *her* has replaced *Estelle's.*

A <u>pronoun</u> is a word used in place of a noun.

Study this list of common pronouns. (Some of the words in the right-hand column may be used as other parts of speech.)

COMMON PRONOUNS

I, me, my, mine, myself
you, your, yours, yourself, yourselves
he, him, his, himself
she, her, hers, herself
it, its, itself
we, us, our, ours, ourselves
they, them, their, theirs, themselves

who, whose, whom, which, that
both, several, few, all
many, more, much, most
one, each, every, some, any
everybody, everyone, someone,
no one

Since a pronoun takes the place of one or more nouns (and sometimes also of words that go with the noun), it must be clear which noun or nouns a pronoun refers to.

NOT CLEAR After Abe fixed Rover's food, *he* cleaned the bowl with *his* tongue.

CLEAR After Abe fixed the dog's food, **Rover** cleaned the bowl with **his** tongue. (Now it is clear that *his* means *Rover's.*)

EXERCISE A   Underline each pronoun in the following sentences. There are twenty of them altogether. (Add 5 points for each correct answer.)

A. There are numerous breeds of dogs, and the American Kennel Club lists <u>most</u> of <u>them</u>.

1. I know a person who owns a cocker spaniel.

2. Usually cocker spaniels grow to about thirteen inches tall, and their maximum weight is about eighteen pounds.

3. Some, of course, are slightly larger, and ours is actually somewhat smaller.

4. They make excellent dogs for apartment dwellers.

5. The cocker spaniel used to be a very popular breed, but it has been supplanted by the poodle.

6. Many who own poodles have their dogs' coats cut so each looks as though it were wearing a coat, boots, and mittens.

7. Since cocker spaniels and poodles are small dogs, both adapt well to city living.

8. Different breeds of dogs are suitable for working and hunting, but most of them are pets and provide companionship for their owners.

9. Lionel has a malamute everyone admires.

10. His sister brought it back with her from Alaska.

EXERCISE B   From the list of pronouns on the preceding page, select a pronoun for each of the blanks in the following paragraph. You may use the same pronoun more than once. (Add 4 points for each correct answer.)

1   Not *everyone* knows that the Dracula legend is partly based
2   on fact. . . . . think that the entire legend is a fiction. Actually
3   . . . . is based on several old tales that told of a fifteenth-century
4   warrior . . . . was known for . . . . cruelty.
5   . . . . was called "Vlad the Terrible" or "Vlad the Impaler."
6   . . . . say that . . . . had ever enjoyed tor-
7   turing . . . . prisoners as Vlad did. . . . . was said
8   that often . . . . kept . . . . locked up in
9   . . . . castle. Because many people feared . . . .,
10 and because . . . . lived for an unusually long period of time,
11 . . . . of the superstitious were afraid Vlad was a vampire,
12 . . . . of the living dead. People began to call . . . .
13 "Dracul." Of course, tellers of legends often exaggerate a person's deeds.
14 . . . . make the person appear better or worse than
15 . . . . really is. Fear and superstition also add exaggerated detail
16 to these stories. . . . . enjoy frightening . . . . with
17 tales of terror. Several years ago, Vlad's tomb was discovered by ar-
18 chaeologists. When . . . . opened . . . .
19 coffin, ... found . . . . was empty.

Adjectives

There are special kinds of words that are used to make other words more definite. Such a special word is known as a *modifier*. It gives additional information which describes or limits the word it modifies.

WITHOUT MODIFIER   The boat sank. (*Which* boat sank?)

WITH MODIFIER   The red boat sank. (*Red* modifies the noun *boat*. It tells which boat sank.)

An adjective is a word used to modify a noun or pronoun.

Most adjectives come before the nouns they modify. They answer the questions *what kind? how many? how much? which one?* or *which ones?*

WHAT KIND?	**towering** cliffs
	swift rapids
	English literature
HOW MANY OR HOW MUCH?	**three** books
	enough money
WHICH ONE?	**this** time
	that chair

In some sentences, adjectives come after the words they modify.

EXAMPLES   Rainfall is **plentiful** here.

The peninsula seems **narrow**.

More than one adjective may be used to modify a noun or pronoun.

EXAMPLES   I want the **big green** book.

They are **tired** and **sleepy**.

The dog, **cold** and **hungry**, looked at us.

There are three special adjectives called *articles*. These are the frequently used words *a, an,* and *the*. You may ignore them in all of the exercises.

EXERCISE A   In the following sentences, fill each blank with a suitable adjective and draw an arrow to the word it modifies. (Add 10 points for each correct answer.)

1   Our ...*history*... teacher gave us a ...*special*... assignment. It

2   must be at least .... pages long. We will have to spend

3   .... hours in the library. Actually, we all think the library

4 is a .... place to study. I am .... to get started.

5 The subject should be .... and must be taken from the

6 chapters we studied. The *Readers' Guide* will be .... in

7 finding this material. The librarian can also give us .... tips

8 on which books to look for. Our teacher will send the ....

9 papers to the essay contest. I want to write a good paper. It would be

10 .... to win .... weeks in Washington, D.C.

EXERCISE B Underline all of the adjectives in the following sentences. Do not include adjectives in book titles and story titles. (Add 5 points for each correct answer.)

A. Washington Irving was the <u>first</u> <u>American</u> writer who won <u>lasting</u> fame in Europe. (3)

1. Even as a young child, he had an adventurous spirit. (2)

2. In his humorous *Sketch Book* he says he "made many tours of discovery into foreign parts and unknown regions of his native city." (5)

3. *Knickerbocker's History of New York,* his first book, was popular and successful. (3)

4. His quaint tales of life in the rural valleys near the Hudson River are delightful even today. (3)

5. Most students have heard of "Rip Van Winkle" and "The Legend of Sleepy Hollow." (1)

6. These stories contain supernatural events. (2)

7. Irving spent many pleasant years in England and Spain. (2)

8. When he returned to this country, he built a comfortable house that he called "Sunnyside," near Tarrytown, New York. (2)

Verbs

A _verb_ is a word that expresses action or helps to make a statement.

Verbs are the backbone of good speaking and writing. They are the words which tell what is happening. Many verbs express actions we can see or hear.

EXAMPLES   The gymnast **flips** in the air.
The Borden twins **sing** in the choir.

Verbs can also express mental action.

EXAMPLES   Inez **wants** to go to medical school
Everyone **thought** that it would rain.

Some verbs consist of more than one word.

EXAMPLES   I **am asking** for a recount of the votes.
Mr. Gray **would have** come if he **had been** invited.

Notice that the verbs are printed in red. The underlined words are called _helping verbs_. Study the following list.

HELPING VERBS

am	is	are	was	does	would
have	has	had	do	will	been
can	could	shall	should	be	
may	might	must	were	did	

When a helping verb is used, the parts of a verb may be separated by another part of speech, as in the following examples:

EXAMPLES   Joan **has** never **come** late to a meeting.
The rain **will** probably **stop** before morning.

EXERCISE A Underline the verb in each of the following sentences. Be sure to include helping verbs. (Add 5 points for each correctly marked sentence.)

A. Our team might well win nearly every game this season.

1. The crowd fills the bleachers in a hurry.

2. Last week we played Burdick School.

3. Their halfback weighs almost two hundred pounds.

4. Our quarterback will catch the ball every time.

5. On one play he dodged around left end.

6. Our team did not block effectively.

7. Burdick's halfback landed on our poor quarterback.

8. In a minute at least six other players had piled on top.

9. Malcolm, our quarterback, suffered a sprained ankle.

10. We will have a substitute quarterback in the game next week.

11. In the summer, other sports take all our time.

12. We will usually play games for individuals or small groups.

13. Many of us took tennis during the spring months.

14. For several years, Jean and I have played tennis in the park.

15. In the early morning, hardly anyone uses the courts.

16. The girl next door plays baseball in the Little League.

17. Her team will probably win the city championship.

18. Her sister has developed a good fast ball.

19. She and Lena often practice together.

20. Many of Lena's friends have suggested Carrie for their team.

EXERCISE B   In the blank spaces, supply a verb which will tell what is happening in the sentence. In some sentences you will need a helping verb to make the meaning clear. (Add 10 points for each correct sentence.)

A. For many years the river *has flooded* every spring.

1. Yesterday our family .... to Weston.

2. I .... my skis at home.

3. Rita .... for Middletown at eight o'clock.

4. She .... her destination by eleven-thirty tomorrow.

5. The fog .... us many times on our way to school.

6. I .... weather like this.

7. Marc .... with his father in the contracting business.

8. If I could, I .... for a summer job in the spring.

9. I .... this assignment soon.

10. From now on, I .... more care with these small jobs.

Linking Verbs

The verbs you have studied so far are verbs that express action. There is a second kind of verb: verbs which help to make a statement. They are called *linking verbs.*

Linking verbs do not show action. They help to make a statement by linking a noun or pronoun to a word or an idea which follows.

EXAMPLES   The tiger **is** ferocious. (*Is* helps to make a statement by linking the noun *tiger* and the adjective *ferocious.*)
Carol **was** the troop leader. (*Was* links the words *Carol* and *leader.*)
The report **seems** long. (*Seems* links the words *report* and *long.*)

COMMON LINKING VERBS

am	were	become	taste
is	being	appear	grow
are	been	remain	look
was	seem	smell	feel

Depending on how they are used in a sentence, *appear, remain, smell, taste, grow, look,* and *feel* may also be action verbs.

LINKING VERB   The flowers **smell** sweet.
ACTION VERB   I **smell** the flowers.
LINKING VERB   The soup **tastes** delicious.
ACTION VERB   We **tasted** the soup.

A linking verb, like an action verb, may need a helper.

EXAMPLES   Howard **has been** absent for two days.
He **did seem** ill on Monday.
I **am feeling** sorry for him.

EXERCISE A   Underline the linking verbs in the following sentences. Be sure to include any helping verbs. (Add 5 points for each correctly marked sentence.)

1. Atlanta is the capital of Georgia.

2. It has become an important center for trade and manufacturing.

3. The state's forests are a major source of wealth.

4. Lumbering has been an important industry since early days.

5. Cotton remains the most valuable farm product in Georgia.

6. Macon is a beautiful old city.

7. This city was the birthplace of Sidney Lanier.

8. Lanier became a well-known poet.

9. Carson McCullers was another native of Georgia.

10. *The Heart Is a Lonely Hunter* has been her most popular novel.

11. Georgia is the largest state east of the Mississippi.

12. Georgians may feel proud of the history of their state.

13. It was once a colony for the unfortunate debtors in English prisons.

14. Savannah was Georgia's first city.

15. The little village on the Savannah River has grown large.

16. Georgia's peach crop has become a famous one.

17. Georgia peaches taste especially sweet.

18. They are best at the time of their harvest.

19. In the spring the peach blossoms smell delightful.

20. The blossoming orchards appear entirely pink.

EXERCISE B   Underline each linking verb in the following paragraph. Do not underline any action verbs. (Add 10 points for each correct answer.)

1. *Bonsai,* a Japanese word meaning "planted in a tray," is the art of growing miniature trees in shallow pots.

2. Bonsai also is the name of a tree that is grown in this manner.

3. The growth is controlled so that the tree will look ancient.

4. If you prune the roots and branches often, the tree becomes stunted.

5. You can shape the tree by tying the branches with wire.

6. Eventually, the tree will appear twisted and windblown.

7. If you like a tree that smells nice, a pine tree or a cherry tree is a good choice.

8. Your choice of container is important too.

9. It should be shallow earthenware and can be plain or glazed.

Adverbs

As its name implies, an *adverb* is a word *added to a verb* to clarify its meaning. It may also be "added to" an adjective or another adverb.

An <u>adverb</u> is a word used to modify a verb, an adjective, or another adverb.

Adverbs answer the question *how? when? where? to what extent?* (*how much?* or *how often?*) In each of the following sentences the adverb (printed in red) modifies the verb.

HOW?	I reviewed **quickly** for the test.
	Tom entered **noisily**.
WHEN?	Mom worked **late**.
	Sharon arrived **yesterday**.
WHERE?	We drove **away**.
	Put the books **there**.
TO WHAT EXTENT?	He works **endlessly**. (*how much?*)
	We have **always** walked to school. (*how often?*)

Adverbs sometimes modify adjectives and other adverbs, but an adverb is never used to modify a noun or pronoun. (Note also that an adverb modifies a verb more often than it modifies an adjective or another adverb.)

MODIFYING AN ADJECTIVE   The campaign was **extremely** successful.

A Morgan is a **very** small horse.

MODIFYING ANOTHER ADVERB   I packed the china **rather** carefully.

The car stopped **too** suddenly.

SOME COMMON ADVERBS

How?	*When?*	*Where?*	*How much?*	*How often?*
easily	soon	here	very	sometimes
safely	now	outside	somewhat	seldom
suddenly	already	there	too	frequently

EXERCISE A   Circle each adverb in the following sentences. Draw an arrow to the word it modifies. (Add 5 points for each correct answer.)

A. We went back to our books.

1. The temperature of the water at the fish hatchery seldom varies.

2. The water never freezes.

3. It comes from unusually large springs.

4. It is very clear water.

5. Steam sometimes rises from warm water.

6. Yesterday I read a pamphlet on preparing oranges for the market.

7. Workers promptly remove spoiled oranges.

8. They always rinse the fruit in cold water.

9. Later the workers sort the oranges by size.

10. Finally they ship the oranges to a packing house.

EXERCISE B Fill in each blank with a suitable adverb and draw an arrow to the word it modifies. In the blank at the end of the sentence, tell which question (*how? when? where? to what extent?*) the adverb answers. (Add 10 points for each correctly marked sentence.)

A. Nikki and Emilio *carefully* made plans for their puppet show.
   how

1. They had . . . . wanted to give a puppet show. . . . .

2. The two . . . . built a puppet theater and made papier-mâché puppets. . . . .

3. Both . . . . painted faces on the puppets. . . . .

4. Nikki and Emilio rehearsed . . . . until they were sure of their parts. . . . .

5. . . . . had they worked so hard. . . . .

6. . . . . the day of the show arrived. . . . .

7. They set up their theater . . . . on the lawn. . . . .

8. The show went . . . .

9. The audience applauded . . . .

10. The two performers decided that they would put on an even better show
    . . . .

Prepositions and Prepositional Phrases

A **preposition** is a word used to show the relationship of a noun or pronoun to some other word in the sentence.

In the following sentences each preposition shows a different relationship between the words *flew* and *clouds*. By changing the preposition, we change the meaning of the sentence.

EXAMPLES   We flew **beneath** the clouds.   We flew **over** the clouds.
We flew **toward** the clouds.   We flew **near** the clouds.

WORDS COMMONLY USED AS PREPOSITIONS

about	before	down	near	under
above	behind	during	of	until
across	beneath	for	on	up
after	beside	from	over	upon
around	between	in	to	with
at	by	into	toward	without

A preposition introduces a group of words. The group of words introduced by a preposition is called a *prepositional phrase*.

A **prepositional phrase** is a group of words which begins with a preposition and ends with a noun or pronoun.

The noun or pronoun at the end of a prepositional phrase is called the *object of the preposition*.

EXAMPLES   across our **street** (noun)   during class **discussion** (noun)
behind the **door** (noun)   without **anyone** (pronoun)

One or more adjectives may modify the object of the preposition.

EXAMPLES   Margaret studied piano for **many** years.
We were sitting on the **front** porch.

EXERCISE A   Find the prepositional phrases in the paragraph below. Circle each preposition and underline each object of a preposition. Notice how line 1 is marked for you. (Add 10 points for each correctly marked phrase.)

1   Mahatma Gandhi wanted his country free (from) Britain. India had

2   been under British control for many years. Gandhi believed that the only

3   way an opponent could be conquered was with love. Violence would bring

13

4 with it further violence. Hate would only breed hate. He felt that his
5 country would gain freedom only through nonviolent means. People
6 struggling for their independence must always keep their anger under
7 control. Anger weakens. Nonviolence is the weapon of the strong. A
8 country could be administered on a nonviolent basis if the majority of
9 the people were nonviolent.

EXERCISE B Put parentheses around each prepositional phrase in the
following sentences. Some sentences contain more than one prepositional
phrase. (Add 4 points for each correct answer.)

A. The discovery (of fire) was an important event (in the history) (of civiliza-
tion).

1. Fire was first made during the Stone Age.

2. Some ancient peoples twisted sticks in holes in wood blocks, and fire
resulted from this action.

3. They also obtained fire from sparks produced when rocks were struck
together.

4. Kindling a fire by these methods is slow and inefficient.

5. People of the Stone Age found keeping a fire alive easier than restart-
ing it.

6. The original source of fire was lightning.

7. A fire started when a tree was struck by lightning.

8. Primitive people took glowing coals of slow-burning wood from this fire
and preserved them in a shelter.

9. The shelter was often deep within a cave.

10. An attendant stayed beside the coals.

11. All fires that the tribe needed were started by these coals.

12. If the tribe moved, the keeper of the fire carried the coals.

13. Sometimes a small fire was kept burning continuously in the shelter.

14. The attendant stayed near the fire and kept it going.

15. For many ancient peoples, fire had religious significance.

16. The Olympic torch is carried to the stadium by marathon runners.

17. From Olympia in Greece, the torch begins its journey.

14

Using Prepositional Phrases

A phrase is a group of related words that is used as a single part of speech. A prepositional phrase may be used to modify a word just as an adjective or adverb does.

EXAMPLE   Erma Bombeck writes articles about suburban life.

In the example above, the phrase *about suburban life* modifies the noun *articles.* It tells *what kind* of articles.

A prepositional phrase used to modify a noun or pronoun is called an adjective phrase.

EXAMPLES   She is the one in the plaid suit.

I ordered a sundae without chopped nuts.

Please bring me the book on the desk.

Everyone in the room was surprised.

A prepositional phrase may modify a noun or pronoun in another prepositional phrase.

EXAMPLE   Cheryl drew a map of the streets near her house.

A prepositional phrase used to modify a verb, an adjective, or an adverb is called an adverb phrase.

EXAMPLES   I studied my lesson with care.   (tells *how* I *studied*)

Mother was working in her office.   (tells *where* Mother *was working*)

Our house is white with green trim.   (modifies an adjective)

We will start early in the morning.   (modifies an adverb)

More than one prepositional phrase may modify the same word.

EXAMPLES   Pete drove his car down Main Street during the rush hour.

After school I stopped at the bakery.

EXERCISE A   Put parentheses around each prepositional phrase and draw an arrow to the word it modifies. (Add 5 points for each correct answer.)

A. One (of the longest rivers) (in America) is the Columbia.

1. The river begins in the Canadian Rocky Mountains.

2. The entire length of this mighty river is 1,270 miles.

3. I am reading a book about the Columbia River.

4. During the Ice Age the Columbia River had a different course.

5. The Grand Coulee Canyon may be the old riverbed of the Columbia.

6. Last summer we traveled through the Grand Coulee region.

7. We visited the site of an ancient waterfall.

8. The width of the waterfall was probably three miles.

9. We went to the Grand Coulee Dam.

10. The Grand Coulee Canyon is located in Washington.

EXERCISE B   Each prepositional phrase in the paragraph below is followed by a blank. Write *adj.* in the blank if the phrase is an *adjective phrase* (modifying a noun or pronoun) and *adv.* if it is an adverb phrase (modifying a verb, adjective, or another adverb). (Add 5 points for each correct answer.)

A SPECIAL TREAT

Some *of you* (1 ....) may have tasted dried litchis. The litchi is a fruit *with a leathery, rough outer shell* (2 ....). If you are lucky enough to live *near a store* (3 ....) that specializes *in oriental produce* (4 ....), you may find fresh litchis *during the summer* (5 ....). If you buy a few *of these delicious fruits* (6 ....), here is one way to eat your dessert and have it too. Peel the outer shell and save it *for later* (7 ....). Bite *into the cool, pearl-white fruit* (8 ....) but be careful *of the pit* (9 ....). When you have finished eating, take the pit *to the sink* (10 ....). Remove any remaining pieces *of pulp* (11 ....) *under the running water* (12 ....). Use a few broken bits *of shell* (13 ....) to cover the bottom *of a small flower pot* (14 ....). Pour some soil *into the pot* (15 ....). Bury the pit horizontally just *below the surface* (16 ....) *of the soil* (17 ....). Water the soil thoroughly and then keep it moist. *In three or four weeks* (18 ....), *with good fortune* (19 ....), a new litchi tree will poke its head *through the soil* (20 ....).

Conjunctions; Interjections; Which Part of Speech?

A conjunction is a word which joins words or groups of words.

By means of conjunctions we bring together words and groups of words to form one complete expression.

EXAMPLES Mark **and** his brother are fishing.
Mark has caught seven fish, **but** Gregg has caught only two.

Conjunctions may also be used in pairs.

EXAMPLES **Neither** Jan **nor** her brother has arrived.
Both Sandra **and** Carol are here.

Here are some frequently used conjunctions.

and	or	either—or	both—and
but	for	neither—nor	

An interjection is a word which expresses strong emotion and is not related grammatically to other words in a sentence.

It is easy to spot an interjection because it is usually separated from the rest of the sentence by punctuation.

EXAMPLES **Whew**! We finally made it!
Well, well, look who's here!
Hey, those seats are reserved for the band.

EXERCISE A The following sentences contain conjunctions and interjections. Underline each conjunction and circle each interjection. (Add 10 points for each correct answer.)

A. (Wow!) The snow <u>and</u> wind are ferocious.

1. Phew! This is certainly a cold and miserable day.

2. I dressed in my warmest clothing, but I am nearly frozen.

3. Neither my coat nor my gloves kept out the wind and the cold.

4. The boys and girls in the safety patrol are stamping their feet to keep warm.

5. Golly, I'm glad I don't have that job.

6. Leo or Marjorie may still have a chance, but I'm sure Brad doesn't.

WHICH PART OF SPEECH?

In this chapter we have studied the eight parts of speech. All words may be classified as one of these parts of speech, yet we cannot tell what part of speech a word is until we see how it is used in a sentence. Many words may be used as more than one part of speech.

A word's use determines its part of speech.

EXAMPLES The **well** ran dry. (noun)
She is looking **well**. (adjective)
She did the job very **well**. (adverb)
The strangers wandered **around**. (adverb)
The squirrel ran **around** the tree. (preposition)
Iron is mined in Minnesota. (noun)
Please **iron** my shirt. (verb)

EXERCISE B In the blank at the right, tell what part of speech each italicized word is *as used in the sentence.* Use the following abbreviations: *n.* for *noun; pron.* for *pronoun; adj.* for *adjective; v.* for *verb; adv.* for *adverb; prep.* for *preposition; conj.* for *conjunction;* and *int.* for *interjection.* (Add 10 points for each correct answer.)

A. Cathy Rigby's *wish* was to be a gymnast.   A. *n.* ....

B. Do you *wish* to be a professional athlete?   B. *v.* ....

1. Some slang sounds like *nonsense.*   1. ....

2. *Nonsense!* He is too young to drive.   2. ....

3. We explored the *river* road.   3. ....

4. The *river* is almost overflowing its banks.   4. ....

5. Carmen *towers* over her mother.   5. ....

6. That *tower* was once a lighthouse.   6. ....

7. We waited a long time *for* Miles.   7. ....

8. We didn't complain, *for* we knew he was busy.   8. ....

9. Finally he said, "Please come *in.*"   9. ....

10. It was cool *in* his room.   10. ....

Chapter Review

EXERCISE A Underline each noun once and each verb twice. Be sure to underline all helping verbs. Put parentheses around prepositional phrases. Not all sentences contain phrases. (Add 10 points for each correctly marked sentence.)

A. The name (of the praying mantis) comes (from the prayerful attitude) (of its front legs).

1. The mantis is an unusual insect of strange habits.

2. This creature lives in many parts of the world.

3. Perhaps twenty different species can be found in America.

4. The mantis is a friend of the farmer.

5. Its victims often include grasshoppers and caterpillars.

6. During its patient wait for victims, the mantis rests motionless on its hind legs.

7. With its strong front legs, it captures other insects.

8. The mantis does not injure plants.

9. The praying mantis is used in greenhouses for insect control.

10. A praying mantis may grow to five inches in length.

EXERCISE B In the following sentences, underline each adjective once and circle each adverb. (Add 4 points for each correct answer.)

A. The ancient Greeks were (very) superstitious about the mantis.

1. The mantis is quite friendly to human beings.

2. The creatures are often curious about their surroundings.

3. The female mantis lays many eggs in a frothy mass.

4. This mass hardens into an egg case, which is fastened tightly to the woody stem of some plant.

5. The tall milkweed is a very common place to find egg cases.

6. You can pick an egg case in the early spring and put it in a tightly closed jar.

7. The baby insects make small holes in the bottom of the case and rapidly swarm out.

EXERCISE C Identify the part of speech of each of the italicized words. Write your answer above the word. Use the following abbreviations: *n.* for *noun;* *pron.* for *pronoun;* *adj.* for *adjective;* *v.* for *verb;* *adv.* for *adverb;* *prep.* for *preposition;* *conj.* for *conjunction;* and *int.* for *interjection.* (Add 5 points for each correct answer.)

A DARING EXPEDITION

1   President Jefferson sent Lewis and Clark *across* the continent. Their

2   task was to find out the extent and *nature* of the vast territory west of

3   the Mississippi. They were to make scientific observations and to estab-

4   lish friendly relations *with* the tribes living in the territory. At first, the

5   men *followed* the Missouri River. *They* traveled by keelboats and flat-

6   boats. During the *first* winter, they stayed at a Mandan village. In April

7   of 1805, they started out *with* a remarkable guide. She was an Indian

8   *woman* whose name was Sacajawea. She carried her two-month-old

9   baby *on* her back. The explorers crossed the Great Divide, *and* still

10   they traveled westward. *Luckily,* Sacajawea met her long-lost brother.

11   Four men were almost killed *during* an encounter with a grizzly bear.

12   In November they reached the mouth *of* the Columbia. In his diary

13   Clark wrote, "*Oh!* the joy!" The expedition *wintered* on the Pacific

14   Coast. By the *next* fall, they had returned to St. Louis. Their reports

15   inspired other *adventurous* Americans. As a result, the *fur* trade also

16   received much impetus. All Americans looked *eagerly* across the conti-

17   nent. This *expedition* blazed the first trail to the West.

Building Vocabulary: Getting Meaning from Context

Following the Cumulative Review lessons in this book (which begin in Chapter Two), you will find lessons designed to help enlarge your working vocabulary—the words and meanings that you recognize in reading and can use to express yourself in writing and speaking. In each vocabulary lesson you will learn ten or more useful words. You will also gain practice with some important vocabulary-building skills that will help you to master other words. As a start, let's review what we mean by *context,* one of the basic vocabulary tools in our ENGLISH WORKSHOP.

See how much the following example tells us about the meaning of *stupor,* the word in red. (*Stupor* does *not* mean *stupid* or *unintelligent.*)

EXAMPLE When the fire alarm woke me, I lay in a **stupor** for several minutes and did not know what was happening.

From this brief *context*—the other words with which *stupor* is used—we can learn a good deal about the word's meaning. We know, for instance, that *stupor* is a noun, and we can guess that it must mean a condition of mental or physical weakness. Probably you could use the word accurately in a similar sentence of your own. However, there are also a number of things that the context does not tell us. It does not tell us the whole meaning of the word, nor does the context show how *stupor* differs from other words that have similar meanings. For this, we need a dictionary.

Check context guesses about a new word by looking up the word's meaning in a dictionary.

If you consulted a dictionary, you would find that *stupor* means a deadening of the mind and senses such as illness, emotional shock, or great drowsiness might cause. The dictionary would also tell you how *stupor* differs in meaning from words with similar meanings, such as *lethargy, apathy,* and *insensibility.*

EXERCISE A Work out the meaning of each italicized word from the context and check your guess in a dictionary. Then, in the space to the left of each number, write the letter of the best meaning from the list below the sentences. Pronunciation charts are given on pages 282–283. (Add 10 points for each correct answer.)

.... 1. If the newspapers continue to *assail* /ə sāl/ Mayor Denby's handling of the school fund, she will surely not run for reelection.

.... 2. Gill is a *competent* /kóm pə tənt/ tennis player, of course, but I doubt that he has much chance of winning the state championship.

21

.... 3. Tom Sawyer was able to *entice* /in tīs/ his friends into whitewashing the fence for him by pretending that it was fun.

.... 4. With a *genial* /jḗn yəl/ smile, Mr. Perez welcomed the new girl and introduced her to the class.

.... 5. Today as never before, poverty and unemployment *menace* /mén is/ the well-being of our community.

.... 6. Maureen Shannesy's sister Debra was the *recipient* /ri síp ē ənt/ of the Anderson Award for sportsmanship and fair play.

.... 7. Because of his bad behavior during the assembly, Wilbur received a *reprimand* /rép rə mand/ from the principal himself.

.... 8. "What makes you say I'm *smug* /smug/?" Tim asked. "After all, you've got to admit that I did win the award."

.... 9. By her *subtle* /sút l/ reasoning, Miss Marple was able to work out the criminal's next move and catch him red-handed.

.... 10. When Martin kept talking about his uncle's swimming pool, we thought he was going to invite us for a swim, but he was merely trying to *tantalize* /tán tə līz/ us.

WORD MEANINGS

a. Of persons, able to do what is needed or required in a particular case; of work, satisfactory, reasonably well done.
b. One who receives.
c. To threaten, especially by making afraid.
d. Skillful and refined, delicate and clever, in thought, expression, behavior, or workmanship.
e. To attack vigorously and repeatedly.
f. A formal and strongly worded rebuke or criticism by someone in authority.
g. Kindly; cheerful and sympathetic.
h. To tease people by offering them again and again something that they want, each time keeping it from them.
i. Sure of one's own goodness and letting others know it; conceited.
j. To lead on, or lure, people, especially into evil, by appealing to their desires or hopes.

EXERCISE B Indicate whether the italicized word is used correctly by circling *C* (for *correct*) or *I* (for *incorrect*) before each statement. (Add 25 points for each correct answer.)

C I 1. The Blakeslees were such *competent* skiers that one of them was always having an accident.

C I 2. Randy was extremely upset by the teacher's *reprimand* and promised never to be late again.

C I 3. For a cat, watching a canary that is out of reach in a cage must be a *tantalizing* experience.

C I 4. Vicki's parents felt extremely proud when Dr. Witly publicly *menaced* her with first prize in the essay contest.

22

Before you begin this first spelling lesson, read the section "A Note on Spelling," on page 281, and become familiar with the two charts that follow it.

These charts will be referred to in many of the spelling lessons in this book. You should find them useful in learning to spell the *majority* of English words. Remember: When a letter appears between a pair of slanted lines, it is the *sound* that is being referred to; a letter alone refers to that *letter* itself.

Spelling: Short Vowels

Have you ever complained that words in English aren't spelled the way they sound? There is hardly a person who hasn't voiced that complaint. If you think English spelling is hopeless and that memorization of every word is the only way to master spelling, try taking another look at the problem.

English spelling is more systematic than you might think. There is no denying that the spelling of our language is full of contradictions and exceptions. As "A Note on Spelling" points out, however, there *is* a relationship between *most* sounds and the letters that represent them. As you saw by looking at the two charts, this is more likely to be true of consonants than of vowels.

This is because *five* overworked letters (*a, e, i, o,* and *u*) must be used to represent about three times that many vowel sounds. But even with vowels, there are certain basic ways in which the sounds are spelled. By mastering these vowel patterns, you will master the spelling of hundreds of words. In this lesson, you will study the five so-called "short" vowel sounds.

Examine the following chart of short vowel sounds and some common spellings and examples of each sound:

Sounds	/a/	/e/	/i/	/o/	/u/
Spellings and Examples	**a:** mat	**e:** bed **ea:** head	**i:** bit	**o:** stop **a:** car	**u:** but **o:** ton

As you can see, short vowel sounds are *usually* represented by only one vowel letter: the sound /i/ is written as *i* in the word *bit;* the sound /a/ is written as *a* in the word *mat.* What exception to this pattern do you find in the chart? Can you give three more words that rhyme with and are spelled the same way as the exception?

EXERCISE A In the blank next to each word below, indicate the *sound* of the italicized vowel (or vowels) by writing *a, e, i, o,* or *u* between the slanted lines. (Add 10 points for each correct answer.)

A. r*e*d ../e/....

1. r*a*ft ../..../.................
2. sp*i*t ../..../.................
3. h*u*t ../..../.................
4. s*e*nt ../..../.................
5. t*o*p ../..../.................

6. d*ea*d ../..../.................
7. cr*a*ck ../..../.................
8. t*a*r ../..../.................
9. thr*i*ft ../..../.................
10. s*o*n ../..../.................

EXERCISE B Twenty of the twenty-five words below contain a short vowel sound. Pick out those twenty words, and decide *which* short vowel sound each word contains. Then write the words in the blanks under the appropriate columns that come after the twenty-five words. (Add 5 points for each correct answer.)

led	bread	note	ugly	wren
slap	brick	clock	tract	day
start	few	trip	come	whiff
slash	mend	health	meat	not
wish	craft	lane	mar	duck

/a/	/e/	/i/	/o/	/u/
....	....	....	....	....
....	....	....	....	....
....	....	....	....	....
....	....	....	....	....
....	....	....	....	....

EXERCISE C Think of two words, *not* used elsewhere in this lesson, for each of the five short vowel sounds given below. Write the new words next to the correct vowel sound. (Add 10 points for each correct answer.)

/a/ ....

/e/ ....

/i/ ....

/o/ ....

/u/ ....

CHAPTER TWO

The Parts of a Sentence

Words are like members of a team. By themselves they cannot do very much, but there is almost no limit to what they can do when they work together. The "team" that words play on is the sentence—a group of words organized to do the job of communicating meaning to other people. English sentences are organized according to certain rules which we must know and follow in order to be understood. In this chapter we shall review the basic rules of sentence construction.

LESSON 13

The Sentence

A <u>sentence</u> is a group of words expressing a complete thought.

INCOMPLETE The woman at the station (What happened to the woman? What did she do? This is not a sentence.)

COMPLETE The woman at the station <u>found a puppy hiding under a car.</u> (This is a sentence.)

INCOMPLETE Disappeared around the corner (What disappeared around the corner? This is not a sentence.)

COMPLETE <u>The fire engine</u> disappeared around the corner. (This is a sentence.)

EXERCISE A Some of the following groups of words are sentences and some are not. Capitals and punctuation have been omitted. In the blank at the right, write *S* if the group of words is a sentence and *NS* if it is not a sentence. (Add 10 points for each correct answer.)

A. walking toward my new school this morning　　　　A. *NS*

1. winning an award for the best design　　　　　　　1. . . . .

2. students of Saxe Junior High School and their parents　2. . . . .

3. Pilar started to water the stock　　　　　　　　　　3. . . . .

4. advised Su-Lin to take the cable car　　　　　　　　4. . . . .

5. the tugboat straining against the long cable　　　　　5. . . . .

6. receiving many gifts at his Bar Mizvah　　　　　　　6. . . . .

7. injuries kept them from competing   7. . . . . . .

8. Beth climbed quickly to the 8000-foot level   8. . . . . . .

9. careful weeding for the garden's best appearance   9. . . . . . .

10. gliding silently through the water in Bob's boat   10. . . . . . .

Every sentence is made of two main parts: the *subject* and the *predicate.*

The subject of a sentence is that part about which something is said.

The predicate of a sentence is that part which says something about the subject.

In the following examples, the subject is separated from the predicate by a vertical line.

EXAMPLES   My older sister | leaves for college this week. (The subject of this sentence is *my older sister.* The predicate, which tells something about the subject, is *leaves for college this week.*)

The cocoa bean | comes from the Amazon jungle.

An army worm | destroys young corn plants.

Professional fighters in ancient Rome | were called gladiators.

EXERCISE B In the following sentences, draw a vertical line to separate each subject from each predicate. (Add 10 points for each correct answer.)

A. The choice of a career | is an important decision.

1. All of us must give the matter a lot of thought.

2. One of my friends has decided to be a reporter.

3. My friend Sharon wants to be a meteorologist.

4. We must soon consider the problem seriously.

5. Our high school courses will affect our future jobs.

6. Some of my friends will take vocational courses.

7. Other boys and girls will prepare for college.

8. I have not decided yet.

9. One of my cousins has just graduated from high school.

10. He is studying forestry at the University of Oregon.

The Simple Subject and the Verb

The subjects you studied in Lesson 13 were all *complete subjects.* The complete subject of a sentence may consist of just one word.

EXAMPLE   **People** | are missing.

Or it may consist of several words.

EXAMPLE   **The people in the overturned boat** | are missing.

Whether a complete subject is long or short, it is always built around a main word (or words) called the *simple subject.*

The simple subject is the main word in the complete subject.

In the following sentences, the *complete subject* is underlined once, and the *simple subject* is printed in red.

EXAMPLES   Our school **library** | closes at three-thirty.

The **girl** in the green suit | lives in our old house.

Chocolate **ice cream** | is my favorite dessert.

The simple subject may consist of more than one word but only if the words are thought of as a single name or object, such as *ice cream* or *Mr. Jefferson* or *high school.*

Like the complete subject, the complete predicate of a sentence may be long or short, but it always contains a main word (or words), the *verb.*

The verb is the main word or group of words in the complete predicate.

EXAMPLES   People | **can save** money by making their own clothes.

My friend | **made** a wool suit for twenty dollars.

Jack | **did** not **take** his package when he left the store.   (The adverb *not* comes between the verb *take* and its helper *did.*)

To find the subject of a sentence, first find the verb and then ask *who?* or *what?* before the verb. Remember that although the simple subject of a sentence may be modified by a prepositional phrase, the simple subject is never found in a phrase.

EXAMPLE   The woman with the dog walked along the street.   (*Who* or *what* walked? *Woman* walked. *Woman* is the simple subject.)

In each of the following sentences, draw a vertical line between the complete subject and the complete predicate. Then underline the simple subject once and the verb twice. Be sure to include helping verbs. (Add 10 points for each correctly marked sentence.)

A. Our trip to Mexico | had already begun at the airport.

1. We arrived at the airport at four o'clock.

2. Our reservations on the flight were quickly confirmed at the desk.

3. The flight attendant welcomed all the passengers aboard the plane.

4. The engines roared into life a few minutes later.

5. All the people on board had by then fastened their seat belts.

6. The takeoff was for me the most exciting part of the flight.

7. Captain Tompkins introduced himself over the intercom.

8. He told us the altitude and speed of the airplane.

9. A delicious dinner was served on plastic trays.

10. The best part of the meal was the dessert.

EXERCISE B Write the simple subject and the verb of each of the following sentences in the blanks at the right. (Add 5 points for each correct answer.)

	Subject	*Verb*

1. Anne Hutchinson left Massachu-
setts for religious reasons. 1. . . . .

2. My hamster is named Tiger. 2. . . . .

3. The poor frightened fox streaked
across the meadow. 3. . . . .

4. The lion in the zoo looks tired. 4. . . . .

5. Everyone in our neighborhood has
signed the petition. 5. . . . .

6. We do not always copy assignments
accurately enough. 6. . . . .

7. You have forgotten your book. 7. . . . .

8. The United Nations occupies sev-
eral imposing structures. 8. . . . .

9. One of us should help him. 9. . . . .

10. Our junior high school dance will
be held next Friday night. 10. . . . .

The Sentence Base

Every sentence in the English language, no matter how long or how short, is built around a simple framework or pattern. We call this pattern the *sentence base.*

THE TWO-PART SENTENCE BASE

A sentence may have a two-part base consisting of the simple subject and the verb.

EXAMPLES People | worked.

Several young people | worked hard all day in the field.

The boy | ran.

The boy in the brown jacket | ran down the corridor.

All of these sentences have a two-part base. The first two sentences are built around the simple subject *people* and the verb *worked.* The second pair is built around the simple subject *boy* and the verb *ran.*

THE THREE-PART SENTENCE BASE

A sentence may have a three-part base consisting of the simple subject, the verb, and the complement.

Some sentences are incomplete without a third part—the *complement.* A complement *completes* the thought expressed by the subject and verb by describing or identifying the subject or by naming the person or thing to which the subject did something.

EXAMPLES My dog | licked | me. (*Me* tells whom my dog licked.)

Her new sweater | looks | beautiful. (*Beautiful* describes the sweater.)

John's father | is | a good lawyer. (*Lawyer* identifies *father.*)

In each of the preceding examples, the third part of the sentence completes the thought of the subject and verb. *My dog licked* leaves the reader hanging. *Who* or *what* did it lick? The complement *me* completes the sentence.

EXERCISE A   Each of the following sentences has a two-part sentence base. Show what the base consists of in each sentence by underlining the simple subject once and the verb twice. Remember that the simple subject is never in a phrase. (Add 10 points for each correctly marked sentence.)

A. Drought can occur during the summer months.

1. The farmers in our area are worrying about the drought.

2. Rain has not fallen for twenty-two days.

3. The summer crops are wilting in the fields.

4. Great cracks have formed in the clay of the riverbeds.

5. The sun creeps into a dusty world every morning.

6. Clouds have sometimes gathered in the sky.

7. They never turn into a storm.

8. The farmers are preparing for irrigation.

9. The disaster area must rely on federal aid.

10. All of us are hoping for rain soon.

EXERCISE B   Each of the sentences below has a three-part base. To show the base in each sentence, underline the simple subject once and the verb twice. Circle the complement. (Add 10 points for each correctly marked sentence.)

A. My favorite constellation is the (Big Dipper).

1. The Big Dipper has seven bright stars.

2. Three of these bright stars form the handle of the dipper.

3. The other four are the bowl.

4. The two end stars in the bowl are called the Pointers.

5. A line through the Pointers reaches the North Star.

6. The North Star is part of the Little Dipper.

7. Sailors in ancient times used the North Star.

8. They could always find north.

9. Another name for the Big Dipper is the Great Bear.

10. Maria Mitchell discovered a comet by using a telescope.

30

The Direct Object

A sentence with a three-part base may contain a subject, a verb, and a direct object. Only an action verb (never a linking verb) can have a direct object.

A **direct object** is a complement, or completer, that receives the action of the verb or names the result of the action.

To find the direct object of a sentence, ask the question *what?* or *whom?* after an action verb. Disregard prepositional phrases and other modifiers.

EXAMPLES   Many cars pass our house. (*What* do the cars pass? *House* is the direct object.)

Jean planned her vacation carefully. (*What* did Jean plan? *Vacation* is the direct object.)

I saw him on the corner. (*Whom* did I see? *Him* is the direct object.)

A direct object is never found in a prepositional phrase.

EXAMPLES   Paula lost a large box of photographs. (*Box* is the direct object. *Photographs* is part of a prepositional phrase and cannot be the direct object.)

Some action verbs may be used either with or without a direct object.

EXAMPLES   Carmen ended her story abruptly. (*What* did Carmen end? *Story* is the direct object.)
The story ended abruptly. (*Abruptly* is an adverb, not a direct object. It answers the question *how?* not *what?* or *whom?*)

EXERCISE A   Circle the direct object in each of the following sentences. (Add 10 points for each correct answer.)

A. Our train left the (station).

1. We baked a cake for Dad's birthday.

2. Our dog chased a little kitten out of our yard.

3. Mother likes carrot juice.

4. Katherine broke her watch recently.

5. Our family ate dinner at a restaurant yesterday.

6. Don washed his car on Thursday.

7. Mari wanted a catcher's mitt for her birthday.

8. We frequently visit Aunt Edith in Brooklyn.

9. I never heard the alarm clock all winter long.

10. I have brought my records for the party.

EXERCISE B In each of the following sentences, underline the verb and circle the direct object if there is one. Remember that a direct object follows an action verb and receives the action of the verb. Not every sentence has a direct object. (Add 5 points for each correctly marked sentence.)

A. The Iroquois had a highly advanced political system.

1. Some of the Iroquois family of nations settled in what is now New York State.

2. Five of these tribes formed a league.

3. They were the Mohawks, the Senecas, the Oneidas, the Onondagas, and the Cayugas.

4. Hiawatha ruled the league for many years.

5. He reformed its laws.

6. The tribes honored Hiawatha.

7. Longfellow used the name of Hiawatha in a poem about a different tribe, the Chippewas.

8. In 1715 the Tuscaroras joined the league.

9. The name of this league was the "Six Nations."

10. We still have some poems by the Iroquois.

11. The Iroquois built dome-shaped houses in winter.

12. In summer they constructed rectangular bark houses.

13. The tribes used bark canoes for traveling along the river.

14. In the winter they wore snowshoes for walking over the snow.

15. The Iroquois made nets for catching fish.

16. They hunted game, such as deer, bear, and buffalo.

17. The tribes cultivated many crops, including corn, squash, and beans.

18. They gathered maple sugar from the trees.

19. They made clothing from animal skins.

20. They celebrated the harvest at the Corn Harvest Festival.

Subject Complements and Linking Verbs

A sentence with a three-part base may consist of a subject, a verb, and a subject complement.

A subject complement is a word which follows a linking verb and describes or identifies the subject of the sentence.

EXAMPLES 1. Karen is a dancer. (*Dancer* identifies the subject *Karen.*)

2. John's sister was the first one in line. (*One* identifies the subject *sister.*)

3. The ambassador seems angry. (*Angry* describes the subject *ambassador.*)

A subject complement may be either a noun (example 1), a pronoun (example 2), or an adjective (example 3). It always occurs in the predicate of a sentence and refers back to the subject. Like the direct object, a subject complement is never found in a prepositional phrase.

Subject complements occur only after *linking verbs*. Linking verbs do not show action. They help to make a statement by linking the subject to a word or idea in the predicate.

EXAMPLES I **am** happy. (*Am* links the subject *I* and the adjective *happy.*)
The bell **sounded** very loud. (*Sounded* links *bell* and *loud.*)
Sally **is** my niece. (*Is* links *Sally* and *niece.*)

The linking verbs include the forms of *to be* (am, is, are—was, were—been) and "sense" verbs like *smell* and *taste.* Any verb for which you can substitute a form of *be* and still make sense is a linking verb.

LINKING VERBS

seem	sound	grow	smell	are	be
look	become	feel	am	was	been
appear	taste	remain	is	were	being

EXERCISE A In the following sentences, underline the linking verbs (including any helping verbs) and draw a circle around the subject complements. (Add 10 points for each correctly marked sentence.)

A. Our new car is the small (one) in the driveway.

1. Mario is often quiet during class discussions.

2. This red sweater is the one I made.

3. Rosa Gomez became a lawyer.

33

4. The squirrels in the woods near our house seem tame.

5. Fresh strawberries taste best with sugar and whipped cream.

6. The lake looks very calm in the moonlight.

7. I am growing weary of studying.

8. Firefighters must remain calm in an emergency.

9. Yesterday I felt sick during lunch period.

10. The perfume smells too strong.

EXERCISE B   In the blank at the end of each sentence, write the subject complement. Some sentences do not contain a subject complement. Write *O* if there is no subject complement in the sentence. (Add 10 points for each correct answer.)

A. My grandmother is my favorite relative.   A. *relative*

B. She has taught me many things.   B. *O*

1. She is always sympathetic to my problems.   1. ....

2. She never becomes upset about my complaints.   2. ....

3. Sometimes she gives good advice.   3. ....

4. Often she just looks happy at our pranks.   4. ....

5. She is the source of endless stories about her
   childhood.   5. ....

6. Grandma left Cuba at seventeen.   6. ....

7. Once she was a reporter for a New York paper.   7. ....

8. She looks very beautiful in the picture we have.   8. ....

9. It is strange to think of her as young.   9. ....

10. Grandma remembers many exciting incidents.   10. ....

Adverb or Adjective?

If we are clear about the work of linking verbs and action verbs, we should never be guilty of mistakes in standard usage like these:

NONSTANDARD   The children sang very *beautiful* at the concert.
NONSTANDARD   The rose smelled rather *sweetly*.

The trouble with the first example is that it makes the adjective *beautiful* modify the action verb *sang*. An action verb needs an adverb modifier.

The trouble with the second example is that it makes the adverb *sweetly* modify the noun *rose*. A linking verb like *smell* in this sentence must be followed by an adjective—a subject complement modifying the subject.

STANDARD   The children sang very beautifully at the concert.

STANDARD   The rose smelled rather sweet.

Many adverbs are formed by adding *-ly* to an adjective (*easily, surely, really*). If you are not sure which word to use, notice whether the verb in the sentence is an action verb (which needs an adverb modifier) or a linking verb (which needs an adjective subject complement). Be especially careful with "sense" verbs like *smell, look,* or *taste,* which may be either linking verbs or action verbs.

LINKING VERB   The cat looked hungry.

ACTION VERB   The cat looked hungrily at the canary.

EXERCISE A   In the blank to the left of each sentence, write *LV* if the verb is a *linking verb* and *AV* if it is an *action verb*. Underline the correct one of the two modifiers in the parentheses. (Add 5 points for each correct answer.)

.... 1. Has she been practicing (regular, regularly)?

.... 2. Melba's voice sounded (beautiful, beautifully) tonight.

.... 3. Traffic is moving (slow, slowly).

.... 4. I was carrying the glass bowl (careful, carefully).

.... 5. The opossum smelled the candy bar (cautious, cautiously).

.... 6. You should treat the animal more (kind, kindly) than that.

.... 7. The villain ran (hasty, hastily) from the stage.

.... 8. Mary McLeod Bethune seemed (courageous, courageously) to us.

.... 9. To me, he looked rather (peculiar, peculiarly) in that getup.

.... 10. You might have explained it more (clear, clearly) than that.

GOOD and WELL *Good* is an adjective. It may be used as a subject complement, but it should *not* be used as an adverb to modify an action verb. *Well* may be used as either an adjective or an adverb. As an adverb, it is the adverb form of *good* and means *capably* or *effectively*.

NONSTANDARD   Michael spoke quite *good* on the subject of conservation.
STANDARD   Michael spoke quite well on the subject of conservation.

As an adjective, *well* means *in good health* or *having a good appearance*.

STANDARD   Howard looks well since his vacation.
STANDARD   Doesn't Mary Jean look well in that costume?

EXERCISE B   Fill the blanks in the sentences with *good* or *well,* depending on the meaning. Remember that *good* should not be used as an adverb. (Add 10 points for each correct answer.)

A. Tom had to go home because he was not feeling ...*well*...

1. She doesn't hear very ....

2. I cannot see the blackboard very .... from where I sit.

3. Your idea for the party seems .... to me.

4. Dad does not look .... since his illness.

5. The orchestra played ....

6. After the accident, it was weeks before I was .... again.

7. A gas turbine engine could run fairly .... on orange juice.

8. I did pretty .... on the test.

9. The cat behaved .... while we were gone.

10. The forecast seemed .... enough to us.

Reviewing the Sentence Base

EXERCISE A   Some of the following sentences have a two-part base and some a three-part base. Indicate the sentence base in each by underlining the simple subject once and the verb twice. Circle the complement (a subject complement or a direct object) if there is one. (Add 10 points for each correctly marked sentence.)

A. Several people were watching the football game.

B. The umpire at third base argued with the shortstop.

1. I walked carefully down the slippery steps.

2. Laura sang a song at the beginning of the assembly program.

3. My parents hired a good mechanic for the engine overhaul.

4. Our ancestors come from many different countries.

5. That devil's-food cake of yours looks delicious.

6. Ellen should not have lost her new watch.

7. All of us stopped at the corner drugstore after the game.

8. The boy on the bicycle hit a tree.

9. The water is boiling briskly in the kettle on the stove.

10. Melodie will mend the saw with the broken blade.

EXERCISE B   The complements in the sentences below are printed in italics. Underline the simple subject of each sentence once and the complete verb twice (including any helping verbs). Then, above each complement, write the abbreviation *d.o.* for a *direct object* or *s.c.* for a *subject complement*. Remember that a direct object follows an action verb and a subject complement follows a linking verb. (Add 10 points for each correctly marked sentence.)

A. Biologists are helping the endangered *whooping crane.* [d.o.]

1. In 1941, naturalists counted only twenty-one *cranes.*

2. These birds spend the *winter* on the Texas gulf coast.

3. Whooping cranes are the tallest *birds* in America.

4. They lay their *eggs* at Wood Buffalo National Park in Canada.

5. Dr. Fred Bard collected crane *eggs* for breeding.

6. The scientist was *confident* about his plan.

7. Sandhill cranes might raise the baby *whooping cranes.*

8. Whooping cranes are much *taller* than their foster parents.

9. They can recognize other *whooping cranes* in a mixed flock.

10. These rare birds are now much more *numerous* than before.

EXERCISE C Circle the seven direct objects in the following paragraph. Do *not* circle any subject complements. (Add 5 points for each correct answer.)

1   At the age of six, I made my only visit to a hospital. My tonsils were

2   taken out. I was in the hospital for a week. I have successfully avoided

3   hospitals ever since. Even the smell of a hospital bothers me somehow.

4   My doctor was an old family friend. I liked her very much. The nurses,

5   too, took good care of me. I don't know the reason for my dislike of

6   hospitals. Whatever the reason, a career as a doctor could never interest

7   me in the least.

Circle the subject complements in the following paragraph. There are thirteen altogether. Do *not* circle any direct objects.

8   My sister and I are very different in this respect. She has always been

9   excellent in science. Now she is studying medicine. My father is skeptical

10   of her ambition. I am not enthusiastic, either. Women doctors were once

11   rare. The situation is changing, however, according to my sister. Women

12   are invaluable in the medical profession. In the Soviet Union today,

13   most of the doctors are women. After medical school, my sister will

14   become a specialist in internal medicine. A doctor in the family may be

15   quite handy, perhaps. I am not really sure about this, however. It is

16   difficult for me to forget my sister as a child. She was always the doctor. I

17   was her unwilling patient.

Compound Subjects and Verbs

When two (or more) connected subjects in a sentence have the same verb, the two (or more) of them together are called a compound subject.

The parts of a compound subject are usually connected by the conjunction *and* or *or.*

EXAMPLES Bicycles and mopeds use the left lane.

Bridget or Marnie will organize the dance.

The planes and trains stopped during the blizzard.

When two (or more) connected verbs in a sentence have the same subject, the two (or more) of them together are called a compound verb.

The parts of a compound verb are usually connected by the conjunction *and, but,* or *or.*

EXAMPLES Caroline Herschel discovered five new comets and described

several star clusters.

The pioneers loaded their wagons and started west.

Cassandra foresaw disaster but could not prevent it.

A sentence may contain both a compound subject and a compound verb.

EXAMPLES Herman and Jack have been here but have already left.

Wind and rain wash soil away and cause erosion.

EXERCISE A In the following sentences, underline the simple subject once and the verb twice. Remember to underline all parts of a compound subject or a compound verb. (Add 10 points for each correctly marked sentence.)

A. The Greek gods punished mortals but always left them hope.

1. The unlucky Pandora received a sealed box from the gods and was curious about its contents.

2. She had been warned not to unseal the box but opened it anyway.

3. Despair and disease flew out of the box and frightened Pandora.

4. Plague and sorrow followed shortly after.

5. At last, hope came from the box and gave comfort to Pandora.

6. Io also suffered a horrible fate but was given hope of a brighter future.

7. Zeus loved her and unintentionally caused her misfortune.

8. She was turned into a calf and was pursued by a gadfly.

9. Hope and knowledge resided with her.

10. One day she would be turned back into a woman and would have a child named Hercules.

EXERCISE B   Fill in the blanks with compound subjects and verbs that make sense. (Add 10 points for each correct sentence.)

1. . . . . and . . . . are among the main causes of accidents on the highway.

2. Angelo carefully . . . . the tomato plants and . . . . the stems to the stakes.

3. . . . . or . . . . would make a good class president.

4. The old judge . . . . sympathetically but . . . . the prisoner back to jail.

5. . . . . and . . . . are my favorite foods.

6. . . . . and . . . . were two presidents whom I admire.

7. On the first spring day we always . . . . to the park and . . . . a few games of baseball.

8. Neither . . . . nor . . . . has been able to decide on a name for their puppy.

9. Jeffrey usually . . . . late at parties and . . . . after everyone else has gone.

10. . . . . and . . . . are two books that I have enjoyed recently.

Simple and Compound Sentences

The sentences that we have studied so far are called *simple sentences*—sentences with one subject-verb base. A simple sentence may contain a compound subject and a compound verb and still have just one subject-verb base.

EXAMPLE   Dogs and children | howl and fight. (This is a two-part sentence base with a compound subject and a compound verb.)

A compound sentence consists of two or more simple sentences usually joined by the conjunction and, but, or, or nor.

To spot a compound sentence, look for two simple sentences joined (usually) by a conjunction. Notice that the conjunction is preceded by a comma.

EXAMPLES   The dogs | are howling, and children | are fighting.

The cowboy | tells | stories, and his stories | grow | better with each telling.

We | walk to school, or Dad | takes | us.

The radio announcer | warned of a storm, but no one | paid | any attention.

In the following example, notice how two simple sentences may be combined to make a compound sentence.

SIMPLE   A careful bicyclist always watches for children.

SIMPLE   Parents appreciate this consideration.

COMPOUND   A careful bicyclist always watches for children, and parents appreciate this consideration.

The following sentences are not compound sentences. Why?

SIMPLE   The rustlers raided the ranch and drove off the cattle. (This is a simple sentence with a compound verb.)

SIMPLE   Henry and another man came to the door. (This is a simple sentence with a compound subject.)

Combine these pairs of simple sentences to make compound sentences. Supply a suitable conjunction and put a comma in front of it. (Add 10 points for each correct sentence.)

A. Tod will tidy up the garage ....,.*or*.... his parents will be disappointed.

1. After the storm, Lauri rang our bell .... we hired her to shovel snow.

2. Another helper came an hour later .... the work was finished.

3. I poured the milk into a small dish .... the kitten would not drink it.

4. You will have to hurry .... you will be late for school.

5. Walt wanted to work after school .... he could not find a part-time job.

6. Sue and I talked about our plans for the class party .... Sue told me about Roxanne's suggestions.

7. Marissa and Janet chose a ride on the roller coaster .... Tricia chose the whip.

8. Ernie has a bad cold .... Jerry has one, too.

9. I have tried to play several musical instruments .... I haven't been very successful.

10. Skin divers must follow safety precautions .... they may be injured.

EXERCISE B In the blank at the left of each sentence, write *S* if it is a simple sentence and *C* if it is a compound sentence. Add a comma wherever necessary in a compound sentence. (Add 20 points for each correct sentence.)

..*C*.. A. Amy likes popular songs, but I prefer classical music.

.... 1. We visited the Grand Canyon and saw sights twice as impressive as Niagara Falls.

.... 2. We were divided into smaller groups and each group was taken on a mule tour.

.... 3. I had read about the Grand Canyon but now I wanted to see every part of it.

.... 4. Some tourists stay on the north rim and observe the changing colors of the canyon.

.... 5. They stand on the edge of the cliff and look at the scenery through viewers.

Chapter Review

EXERCISE A   Some of the following are simple sentences, and others are compound sentences. A few are not sentences at all. In the blank at the left, write *S* for simple sentence, *C* for compound sentence, or *NS* for the groups of words that are not sentences. (Add 10 points for each correct answer.)

...*S*...   A. My science teacher has gone skiing all over the world.

....   1. In the ski troops during the Korean conflict.

....   2. They trained in Colorado and were shipped overseas in the dead of winter.

....   3. Skiing under combat conditions is different from skiing for fun, and many soldiers had accidents.

....   4. Bullets and frostbite were their main dangers.

....   5. After the war my teacher lived in Albany, New York.

....   6. He liked to ski in the Adirondacks, and he went skiing almost every weekend.

....   7. In Michigan, while in school under the GI Bill.

....   8. He and his roommate went skiing on the sand dunes.

....   9. On their honeymoon he and his wife skied in the Alps and enjoyed it very much.

....   10. His ambition is to go skiing in Peru in July.

EXERCISE B   Underline the simple subject once and the verb twice in each of the following sentences. Some sentences have compound subjects and verbs. Others are compound sentences. (Add 10 points for each correctly marked sentence.)

1. Isadora Duncan was born in the United States but gained most of her success in Europe.

2. She and her family moved to Europe in 1899.

3. Isadora's training and experience were in classical ballet.

4. She objected to the rigidity of ballet and experimented with freedom of movement.

5. She abandoned the classical style and explored the possibilities of interpretative dancing.

43

6. Dancers should reflect the rhythms of nature in their movements, and their dances should show a free but controlled body.

7. The traditional ballet costume was abandoned, and toe shoes were replaced by bare feet.

8. Isadora and her followers performed to the music of contemporary composers.

9. She met Michel Fokine, and together they worked on dances with Greek themes.

10. Many of today's modern dance companies owe a debt to Isadora and recognize her as a pioneer in modern dance technique.

EXERCISE C   Underline all of the complements in the following sentences. Write the abbreviation *d.o.* for *direct object* or *s.c.* for *subject complement* above the proper word. (Add 10 points for each correctly marked sentence.)

A. My parents bought a Persian *d.o.* rug for the living room.

B. It looked *s.c.* beautiful to me.

1. Margaret Mead is a noted anthropologist.

2. I read this book in a hurry.

3. Raccoons are good swimmers.

4. A bear frightened the campers yesterday.

5. Beavers build dams under water.

6. A grasshopper's color protects it from its enemies.

7. Birds are enemies of grasshoppers.

8. Geraldo Rivera is famous for his investigative reporting.

9. He won a great victory against two British ships.

10. Your idea seems very silly to me.

EXERCISE D   Underline the correct word from the pair in parentheses. (Add 20 points for each correct answer.)

1. This Lady Baltimore cake smells (delicious, deliciously).

2. Since I ate that clam stew, I don't feel so (well, good).

3. Did you do (good, well) on the history test?

4. Toni played her part in the school play (perfect, perfectly).

5. Laura skis (good, well) for a beginner.

44

Cumulative Review

A Indicate the part of speech of each italicized word in the paragraph below by writing the appropriate abbreviation above the word. Use these abbreviations: *n.* for *noun, pron.* for *pronoun, adj.* for *adjective, v.* for *verb* (including helping verbs), *adv.* for *adverb, prep.* for *preposition, conj.* for *conjunction,* and *int.* for *interjection.* (Add 2 points for each correct answer.)

FRIENDS AND STATESMEN

1   Thomas Jefferson *and* John Adams *were* two *of* the most *interesting*
2   leaders of the American Revolution. *During* the Revolution *they* worked
3   *closely together* as *members* of the Continental Congress. *Later,* Jefferson
4   was Vice-President while Adams was President. In 1800 Jefferson *ran*
5   for President *against his* old *friend* and *won* the election *by* seven *electoral*
6   votes. *Adams* had been *unpopular* during his *administration,* and the
7   *bitter* election *cost* the two men their *friendship.* Adams *retired from*
8   public *life.* Jefferson followed *him* in 1809, *at* the end of his second term.
9   *Well,* out of *politics,* the two men *gradually* became *friendly* again.
10   They *wrote* to each other *often. Their* letters are a record of two *lively*
11   *gentlemen whose* minds remained *active* as long as they lived. The two
12   friends died *within* hours of one another on July 4, 1826, the *fiftieth*
13   anniversary of their country's *independence,* to which both *had* contrib-
14   uted *so* much. As Adams lay dying, he did not *know* that his friend had
15   *died* a few hours *earlier.* His last *words* were, "Thomas Jefferson *still*
16   *lives.*"

B Underline the complete verbs in the following sentences, including any helping verbs, and draw a circle around the helping verbs. (Add 20 points for each correctly marked sentence.)

1. I have my tickets for tomorrow's game.

2. I have spent too much time at basketball games.

3. A person can waste too much time that way.

4. I gave my tickets to my little brother.

5. You should have seen the expression on his face.

C Circle each adverb in each of the following sentences and draw an arrow to the word it modifies. (Add 10 points for each correct sentence.)

1. Rosalie often exercises in the early morning.

2. She tirelessly does fifty sit-ups and fifty push-ups.

3. Usually she follows her exercises with a good breakfast.

4. She is in very good physical condition.

5. If she does well in competition, she may try to become a professional swimmer.

Underline each adjective in the following sentences and draw an arrow to the word it modifies.

6. Some people believe that regular exercise is good for your eyes.

7. You can exercise them by looking first at a nearby object and then at a faraway object.

8. By doing this exercise you strengthen the muscles which control the focus of your eyes.

9. These muscles are called the ciliary muscles.

10. Can they really be exercised like any other muscles?

D Put parentheses [( )] around all the prepositional phrases in the following paragraph. Underline the object of each preposition. (Add 5 points for each correct answer.)

1   Our neighbor Mr. Holmes has bought an old pipe organ from a movie

2   theater. He has installed it in the basement of his house. Parts of it have

3   also spilled into the garage. He is extremely proud of his new possession.

4   When he plays it during the summer, all of the windows rattle in the

5   houses on the next block.

Building Vocabulary: Exploring Word Histories

Suppose you could enter a time machine and travel back to the England of a thousand years ago. You would find the people speaking an English so different from the language we speak today that you would not be able to understand it at all. The reason is that our language has changed greatly. Old words have dropped out of use or changed their meaning. New words have been borrowed from other languages to meet the needs of changing experience. Some of these foreign words changed in meaning when they were taken into English. Others, however, carry over much of their original meaning. Often a knowledge of the history, or *derivation,* of borrowed words can help us to pin down their precise meaning.

Use a dictionary to study the derivation of a word.

Most large dictionaries trace a word's derivation back to its original language. The derivation will include the foreign word or words from which the modern English word comes, the language of the foreign word (shown by an abbreviation—*F.* for *French, L.* for *Latin, Gr.* for *Greek*), and the meaning of the word in the original language.

If you looked up the derivation of *thoroughfare,* you would find that it combines two Anglo-Saxon words meaning "through" and "go." A *thoroughfare* is a public road that "goes through." The modern word *thruway* is formed in much the same way and carries the same idea.

The word *metropolis,* which comes to us from Greek, usually means any large city. It has a more precise meaning, however, and the derivation provides a clue to it. *Metropolis* is formed from *meter* (mother) and *polis* (city); to the Greeks, who were great colonizers, a *metropolis* was the "mother city," the original center around which a new colony was built. The more precise meaning of *metropolis* is not just any large city but the central or most important city in any region.

EXERCISE A   Using a large dictionary, give the derivation of the following words: (1) the foreign word(s) from which each word comes; (2) the original language; (3) the meaning of the original word(s); (4) the meaning of the English word. (Add 2½ points for each correct answer.)

A. metropolis (1) *meter + polis.*   (2) *Greek.* ....   (3) *mother, city.*

   (4) *the largest and most important city of a region* .....

1. adjacent (1) ....   (2) ....   (3) ....

   (4) ....

2. alternate, *v.* (1)............... (2)............. (3)...............
(4) ....

3. amphibious (1)............... (2)............. (3)...............
(4) ....

4. auspicious (1)............... (2)............. (3)...............
(4) ....

5. dominate (1)............... (2)............. (3)...............
(4) ....

6. expire (1).................. (2)............. (3)...............
(4) ....

7. heretic (1)................. (2)............. (3)...............
(4) ....

8. preamble (1)............... (2)............. (3)...............
(4) ....

9. secluded (1)............... (2)............. (3)...............
(4) ....

10. vigilance (1)............... (2)............. (3)...............
(4) ....

EXERCISE B   To the left of each number, write the letter of the best
meaning for the italicized word. (Add 10 points for each correct answer.)

.... 1. the *adjacent* house

.... 2. *alternate* with someone

.... 3. an *amphibious* reptile

.... 4. an *auspicious* beginning

.... 5. *dominate* a meeting

.... 6. *expire* suddenly

.... 7. a declared *heretic*

.... 8. begin without *preamble*

.... 9. a *secluded* location

.... 10. constant *vigilance*

a. an opening statement

b. to control or rule, master

c. separated, cut off from others

d. to change regularly, by turns

e. watchfulness for danger

f. living on land and in water

g. favorable, promising

h. to breathe out; to die

i. nearby

j. one who does not conform to
an established belief

Spelling: Long Vowels

The long vowel sounds in English are more complicated than the short ones you learned about in Lesson 12. Each long vowel sound can be spelled in four, five, or even six different ways. Look at the chart below and see if you can figure out any patterns in the spelling of long vowel sounds:

Sounds	/ā/	/ē/	/ī/	/ō/	/ū/
Spellings and Examples	VCe: same ai: wait ay: say ei: weigh	VCe: Pete ee: weed ea: meat e: she ie: field ei: deceive	VCe: mine igh: sigh y: why ie: pie	VCe: lone oa: coat ow: crow oe: toe o: so	VCe: June oo: boot ew: few ue: sue o: to

As you can see by examining the top row of example words (*same*, *Pete*, etc.), many words containing a long vowel sound are spelled with a single vowel letter followed by a single consonant letter followed by the letter *e*. (Perhaps you remember from your reading of "A Note on Spelling" that this is what the letters **VCe** on the chart stand for.) The final *e* in such words is often thought of as "silent" because it is not pronounced. It is, however, an important letter, for it indicates that the vowel that comes before the final "silent" *e* has a long sound. Without that silent *e* we have an entirely different word: *hop—hope, tub—tube,* etc.

Another look at the chart will tell you that long vowel sounds are frequently spelled with a combination of *two* vowels: *wait, coat, boot.* Name some other examples.

You will simply have to remember the correct spelling of each long vowel sound in various groups of words.

EXERCISE A Pronounce each word below. Then, in the blank, indicate the sound of the italicized letter (or letters) in the word by writing ā, ē, ī, ō, or ū between the pair of slanted lines. (Add 4 points for each correct answer.)

1. h*igh* ../..../..............
2. r*u*de ../..../..............
3. fr*ee* ../..../..............
4. bl*ow* ../..../..............
5. m*ew* ../..../..............
6. g*o* ../..../..............
7. h*ea*t ../..../..............
8. l*ie* ../..../..............
9. s*oo*n ../..../..............
10. b*o*ned ../..../..............
11. y*ie*ld ../..../..............
12. sch*e*me ../..../..............

49

13. p*ai*n ../..../................   19. gr*oa*n ../..../...........

14. f*l*y ../..../.................   20. l*a*me ../..../...........

15. conc*ei*ted ../..../...........   21. f*i*le ../..../................

16. r*a*y ../..../................   22. h*oe* ../..../...............

17. gl*ue* ../..../................   23. n*eigh* ../..../............

18. h*e* ../..../.................   24. d*o* ../..../................

25. sh*ow*n ../..../..............

EXERCISE B Choose two different ways of spelling *each* of the five long vowel sounds you have learned. In each set of blanks, write words (other than those used in this lesson) whose spellings illustrate the two ways you selected. (Add 10 points for each correct answer.)

	FIRST WAY	SECOND WAY
/ā/	....	....
/ē/	....	....
/ī/	....	....
/ō/	....	....
/ū/	....	....

EXERCISE C Study all of the words taught in this lesson. Say the word; look at the word; close your eyes and "see" it in your mind; spell the word with your eyes closed; write the word. Then be ready to write the words as your teacher dictates them. (Add 4 points for each correct answer.)

REVIEW EXERCISE Be prepared to write the following words from dictation. (Add 10 points for each correctly spelled word.)

1. health
2. not
3. tar
4. brick
5. duck
6. ugly
7. bread
8. clock
9. top
10. craft

CHAPTER THREE

Building Sentences with Adjective Clauses

Every time we try to describe a person, a thing, or an action, we use a modifier of some kind. English is especially rich in the kind of modifier called an *adjective*. Yet quite often we cannot find any one word that says exactly what we mean. Instead of a one-word modifier, we must use a whole group of words to make our meaning clear. The prepositional phrase is one kind of word group that we can use when no one-word modifier will do the job. The adjective clause, which we shall study in this chapter, is another.

LESSON 26

What Is a Clause?

A clause is a group of words that contains a verb and its subject and is used as part of a sentence.

Each of the following sentences contains two clauses. The subject and verb in each clause are underlined.

EXAMPLES I prefer Eudora, who is enthusiastic.

Mrs. Bell, whom I admire so much, is a talented woman.

Jane wore the necklace that Iris had given her.

We have a visiting squirrel which we feed.

An independent clause expresses a complete thought and can stand by itself as a sentence.

In other words, a simple sentence consists of just one independent clause. A *compound sentence* consists of two or more independent clauses.

INDEPENDENT CLAUSES   I prefer Eudora.
                             Mrs. Bell is a talented woman.
                             Jane wore the necklace.
                             We have a visiting squirrel.

TWO INDEPENDENT CLAUSES   Mrs. Bell is a talented woman, and I admire her.

A subordinate clause does not express a complete thought and cannot stand by itself.

51

EXERCISE A Some of the following groups of words express a complete thought and could be used in sentences as independent clauses. Others do *not* express a complete thought and are therefore subordinate clauses. In the blank to the right of each item, write *ind.* for an *independent clause* and *sub.* for a *subordinate clause*. Put a capital letter at the beginning of each independent clause and a period at the end. (Add 10 points for each correctly marked item.)

A. It has been an exciting week for us.   ...*ind.*...

1. we discovered an aluminum canoe   ....

2. which we found washed up on the lake shore   ....

3. on the bow it had the name *Limber Lost*   ....

4. which is the name of a big estate across the lake   ....

5. from which it broke loose during last night's storm   ....

6. reluctantly Dan offered to take it back   ....

7. which Jay helped paddle   ....

8. whom they saw coming across the lake   ....

9. we will save the ten-dollar reward for our own canoe   ....

10. which we saw in the mail-order catalogue   ....

EXERCISE B The first subordinate clause in the following paragraph is underlined; underline the five remaining subordinate clauses. (Add 20 points for each correct answer.)

1   Yesterday we earned more money toward the canoe that we want to

2   buy. After the rainstorm Jay noticed many cars which seemed very dirty.

3   We rang all the doorbells in our neighborhood. Several of the people

4   whom we approached were glad to have us wash their cars. I remember

5   one woman whose three children helped me to wash their station wagon.

6   We charged a dollar for every car which we washed and polished. Today

7   we are stiff and sore from our work. The twelve dollars which we earned

8   makes our aches and pains feel better.

Adjective Clauses and Relative Pronouns

The subordinate clauses you have studied so far all began with *who, whom, whose, which,* or *that.* These five pronouns are called *relative pronouns.*

A relative pronoun is a pronoun which begins a subordinate clause and relates it to another word or idea in the sentence.

EXAMPLES   Ellen is a girl who enjoys singing.

My neighbor, whom I see at work every day, is on vacation.

He has a dog which barks at loud noises.

I know someone whose brother is in the marines.

This is the lawn furniture that was advertised.

In each of the examples the relative pronoun refers to a noun or pronoun, and the clause as a whole gives additional information about this noun or pronoun. The clause does the work of an adjective.

An adjective clause is a subordinate clause which is used as an adjective to modify a noun or pronoun.

EXERCISE A Underline the adjective clauses in the following sentences. Watch for the relative pronouns which signal the beginning of an adjective clause. (Add 20 points for each correct answer.)

1. Ricardo plays jai alai, which is a popular Spanish handball game.

2. Dorothy Sayers was a scholar and teacher who also wrote detective stories.

3. The cat with the white ears is the one that I want.

4. This is the music which we are playing in the Thanksgiving program.

5. Laura Gilpin is the one whose photographs are on display.

EXERCISE B Underline the adjective clauses and circle the word each clause modifies. The first sentence is done for you. (Add 2½ points for each correct answer.)

AARON BURR

1   Aaron Burr, who is considered one of the most notorious figures in

2   American history, led an interesting life. In 1775 he joined the American

       53

3 army in Boston, which was under the control of Benedict Arnold. Burr
4 fought in the Quebec campaign, which brought him to the attention
5 of General Washington, who was commander of all the American forces.
6 Friction arose between Burr and Washington, whose skills as a general
7 Burr little respected. After the Revolution Burr became a lawyer and
8 rose in New York politics, bringing him into conflict with Alexander
9 Hamilton, whom he had met during the war. Their constant political
10 competition and mutual dislike of each other eventually brought about
11 the gun duel that has blackened Burr's name. A coroner's inquest
12 brought a verdict of murder against Burr, who was then Vice-President.
13 Burr fled the state.

14   Thomas Jefferson was also a political opponent whose actions helped
15 bring about Burr's downfall. In 1800, Jefferson, who was running for
16 the Presidency, and Burr, who was running for the Vice-Presidency,
17 received the same number of votes. Electors cast two ballots that
18 did not indicate the preferred candidate who would be
19 the President. The one that received the greatest number of votes
20 became President. The House of Representatives cast thirty-six ballots
21 to break the tie before choosing the man who would be President. This
22 conflict weakened a relationship that at best had been cold. The admin-
23 istration, whose head was Jefferson and whose second-in-command was
24 Burr, was filled with internal conflict.

25   After his term as Vice-President, Burr traveled in the West. Some
26 say he planned to invade Mexico and depose its ruler, whose place he
27 would then take. Others say he planned to detach from the United States
28 part of the Southwest, which was politically disenchanted with Jefferson.
29 Whatever Burr's plan, Jefferson had him tried for treason, an accusation
30 that he was cleared of by John Marshall.

Clauses Beginning with WHO, WHOM, or WHOSE

Who, whom, and *whose* introduce adjective clauses referring to people.

Use who when the relative pronoun is the subject of the adjective clause.

EXAMPLE Anna Ella Carroll, who was acclaimed as a military genius, played an essential part for the Union in the Civil War.

Use whom when the relative pronoun is used as an object in the adjective clause.

EXAMPLES Joe Louis, whom I have seen on television, held the heavyweight title longer than anyone else. (*Whom* is the direct object of the verb *have seen.*)

Jim Braddock, from whom he won the title, had beaten Max Baer. (*Whom* is the object of the preposition *from.*)

Use whose to introduce an adjective clause showing possession.

EXAMPLES Lady Godiva, whose ride is familiar to most of us, rode through the streets to protest her husband's cruel oppression of the people.

Maya Angelou is a writer whose books interest me.

EXERCISE A Underline the adjective clauses in the following sentences. Circle the word each clause modifies. Notice that the word modified by the clause is also the word to which the relative pronoun refers. (Add 10 points for each correctly marked sentence.)

A. The Puritans banished (Roger Williams), who had dared to criticize their actions.

1. The Pilgrims were the people who founded Plymouth Colony in Massachusetts.

2. Susanna Wesley was a person for whom religion was a crucial issue.

3. Rosemary Casals is a tennis player who has won many matches.

4. Sarah Bernhardt, whom we remember as "the divine Sarah," made her acting debut at seventeen.

5. Tracy Austin, who is a famous tennis player, won the U.S. Open at an early age.

6. Shirley Chisholm, whose candidacy for the Presidency in 1972 drew much attention, did not run in 1976.

7. Elizabeth I, whom you may have studied about in a history course, ruled England for forty-five years.

8. Many of the people who started for California during the gold rush were quite ignorant about life there.

9. Gertrude Stein, whose salon was visited by writers and artists, wrote *Three Lives.*

10. Golda Meir, whom many remember, led her country in a time of crisis.

EXERCISE B In the following sentences, fill in the blanks with *who, whom,* or *whose.* (Add 10 points for each correct answer.)

A. I have a letter from the French girl with ... *whom* ... I correspond.

1. The Huffords, ... store is next to the railroad station, sell the thickest milkshakes in town.

2. People for . . . . fishing has a special appeal will enjoy the lakes and streams of Kings Canyon National Park.

3. We all respect Mr. Sands, ... classes are never dull.

4. Mrs. Peters is the person to . . . . I gave the note.

5. I gave an apple to Sean, with . . . . I ate lunch.

6. This article is about Harper Lee, ... wrote *To Kill a Mockingbird.*

7. I will vote for the candidate for . . . . I campaigned.

8. Phillis Wheatley was an early American poet . . . . traveled widely in England.

9. Each year the national parks are visited by people for . . . . a trip to a scenic site is an adventure.

10. The Grand Canyon impressed my sister, ... travels have included many national parks.

Clauses Beginning with WHICH or THAT

Use which to introduce an adjective clause when referring to an animal, place, or thing, but not to a person.

EXAMPLES   This old magazine, which I found in our attic, belonged to my grandfather.

Our musical show, which was given on Friday night, played to a packed house.

Use that to introduce an adjective clause when referring to a person, animal, place, or thing.

EXAMPLES   The road that runs past our farm is rough.

Here are the plans that we made last night.

There is the boy that I talked to yesterday.

In many sentences, either *which* or *that* may be used correctly.

EXAMPLES   Mount St. Helens is the volcano which erupted.
Mount St. Helens is the volcano that erupted.

The important thing to remember is that *which* is *never* used to refer to people.

NONSTANDARD   The first player *which* I saw was Luis Tiant.
STANDARD   The first player that I saw was Luis Tiant.

EXERCISE   Underline the adjective clauses in the following sentences. Circle the word each clause modifies. (Add 5 points for each correct answer.)

1. Gold is a metal which has been valued since ancient times.

2. Gold and platinum are the two metals that are always found in pure form.

3. Gold, which is called a "noble metal," does not react with many other chemicals.

4. Gold is the metal which is most "malleable," or easy to shape.

5. It can be beaten into a sheet which is thinner than a human hair.

6. The Inca gold ornaments, which were made before Columbus reached America, are as untarnished as on the day they were made.

7. Colombia has a museum in which are displayed these beautiful gold objects.

8. The Spanish, who heard about the gold, plundered Inca cities.

9. Today, the property that is most valuable in gold is its ease in conducting electricity.

10. It is this quality that makes it useful in space exploration.

REVIEW EXERCISE Underline the correct relative pronoun in parentheses. Check yourself (a) by finding the word to which the pronoun refers and deciding whether it names a person or a thing; and (b) by deciding whether the pronoun is used as an object of a preposition (requiring the *whom* form). (Add 10 points for each correct answer.)

1. People (who, which) collect rocks are called "rock hounds."

2. Ethel Lee is the one to (who, whom) I lent my bicycle last week.

3. The Rosenbergs' new dog, (whom, which) they got from the Humane Society, is part setter and part bulldog.

4. Most of the boys and girls (who, which) live in the South do not have the opportunity to go ice-skating on frozen lakes in the winter.

5. The newsdealer at the end of the block, from (who, whom) we buy our paper, received a medal.

6. At the party I met a group of people with (whom, which) I got along very well.

7. Aunt Stephanie, (who, whose) husband is a major in the air force, is visiting us next week.

8. Our club's new president, for (whom, which) I have great personal respect, is a good speaker but a poor organizer.

9. Uncle Ezra, after (who, whom) my brother Zeke is named, was once an amateur boxer.

10. The woman in the front row, at (whom, which) you were staring so fixedly, is actually Governor Ella Grasso.

Placement of Adjective Clauses

An adjective clause should usually come right after the word it modifies.

Like most language rules, this one is for the sake of clarity.

UNCLEAR   I borrowed a **book** from the library *which I later lost.* (What did I lose? the library?)

CLEAR   I borrowed from the library a **book** which I later lost. (The phrase *from the library* has been moved forward so that the adjective clause now follows *book,* the word it modifies.)

ALSO CLEAR   I lost the **book** which I had borrowed from the library. (This rearrangement of the sentence also makes the meaning clear.)

UNCLEAR   I fixed some **meat scraps and gravy** for the dog *which smelled delicious.* (Did the dog smell delicious?)

CLEAR   For the dog I fixed some **meat scraps and gravy** which smelled delicious. (This arrangement puts the appetizing smell where it belongs. The phrase *for the dog* has been moved to the beginning of the sentence so that the clause can come right after the words it modifies.)

ALSO CLEAR   The meat scraps and gravy which I fixed for the dog smelled delicious. (Note the rearrangement. The independent clause has been changed to a subordinate clause, *which I fixed for the dog.)*

EXERCISE   Clarify the following sentences by rearranging the word order so that the adjective clause immediately follows the word it modifies. (Add 10 points for each correct sentence.)

A. Our car is being repaired at the garage which was in an accident. .....

Our car, which was in an accident, is being repaired at the garage.

1. The man has bought a new airplane who is taking flying lessons. .....

. . . .

. . . .

2. Ellen will receive many cards whose birthday is today. ....

. . . .

. . . .

3. Anita is putting on shows for children in hospitals that are very entertaining. ....

....

....

4. I was reading a book in the library which was written by James Baldwin. ....

....

....

5. My brother is supposed to walk the dog every morning that lives next door. ....

....

....

6. The woman is on vacation in Canada who asked me to deliver the message. ....

....

7. From the tower we could see three states which we visited Saturday morning. ....

....

....

8. The truck is delivering a piano that is parked in the driveway. ......

....

....

9. The movie star looks just like my cousin Charlie whom we saw in the movie tonight. ....

....

....

10. We are wrapping the gifts to our cousins that will be sent through the mail.

....

....

....

Using Adjective Clauses

Two simple sentences about the same person, place, animal, or thing may be combined by changing one to an adjective clause.

TWO SENTENCES   We were anxiously awaiting Judy. We had planned a surprise party *for her*.

ONE SENTENCE   We were anxiously awaiting Judy, <u>for **whom** we had planned a surprise party</u>. (*For whom* replaces *for her* and moves to the head of the clause.)

TWO SENTENCES   At eight o'clock I met Bill Stewart. *He* is my best friend.

ONE SENTENCE   At eight o'clock I met Bill Stewart, <u>**who** is my best friend</u>. (*Who* replaces *he*.)

TWO SENTENCES   I met Mrs. Jenkins. *Her* husband is my cousin.

ONE SENTENCE   I met Mrs. Jenkins, <u>**whose** husband is my cousin</u>. (*Whose* replaces *her*.)

Writers often omit the relative pronoun in sentences that are not too complicated. The placement of the clause makes the meaning of the sentence clear, even without the relative pronoun.

EXAMPLES   She is the one ∧ ~~whom~~ <u>I talked to yesterday</u>.

The boat ∧ ~~which~~ <u>we sailed in</u> had just been launched.

EXERCISE   Combine each of the following pairs of sentences into one sentence by changing the italicized sentence to an adjective clause. Place the clause next to the word it modifies. (Add 10 points for each correct sentence.)

A. Jerry is one of our best athletes. *He is not very tall.* *Jerry, who is not very tall, is one of our best athletes.*

1. We interviewed Gloria Steinem. *She is an editor for* Ms. *Magazine.*

....

....

2. I saw Mr. Ward. *His blue eyes twinkled at the sight of a customer.*

....

....

3. After school we met two friends. *They asked us to play tennis.* ....

....

....

4. Aardwolves are striped African mammals. *They feed chiefly on insects.*

....

....

5. The Arctic was once a mysterious area. *It was known only to a handful of explorers.* ....

....

....

6. Roberto Clemente died in a plane crash. *He was going to the aid of Nicaraguan earthquake victims.* ....

....

....

7. Malvina Hoffman was a famous sculptor. *Her works can be seen at the Chicago Field Museum.* ....

....

....

8. Aunt Nancy solved the algebra problem in a hurry. *We can always depend on her.* ....

....

....

9. Jane Addams worked for better housing. *She founded a settlement house in Chicago.* ....

....

....

10. I delivered the package to Shirley Morrow. *You met her at my house.*

....

....

Chapter Review

EXERCISE A   Underline the adjective clauses in the following sentences and circle the words they modify. (Add 5 points for each correct answer.)

1. I looked intently at the pictures, which seemed so appropriate on the walls of the beautiful living room.

2. A portrait that hung on one wall interested me particularly.

3. It was the work of a famous artist who lives in California.

4. I admired the artist's subtle use of lavender, which was a prominent color in the portrait.

5. Deeper purple tones, which blended beautifully with the other colors in the picture, created a tranquil mood.

6. The artist had captured a smile that reminded me of the *Mona Lisa*.

7. Yet there was a haughty expression which puzzled me.

8. The young woman who smiled seemed somehow aloof.

9. Perhaps she was a person whose moods changed easily.

10. She must have been someone whom the artist greatly admired.

EXERCISE B   Combine each of the following pairs of sentences by changing the italicized sentence to an adjective clause. Use the relative pronoun shown in parentheses. Be sure to place each clause immediately after the word it modifies. (Add 20 points for each correct sentence.)

A. I am wearing a new sweater. *Louisa made it for me.*   (that). *I am wearing a new sweater that Louisa made for me.*

....

1. That collie belongs to the Lindens. *They are our next-door neighbors.* (who)..

....

2. Ronald has a new car. *He has bought air conditioning for it.*   (which).

....

....

3. Mrs. Olson contributed some canned food for our drive. *She owns a grocery store on Park Street.* (who) . . . .

. . . .

4. Here is a P. L. Travers story. *I found it in a book in my grandparents' attic.* (that) . . . .

. . . .

5. Betty is the star of our musical. *Her voice is lovely.* (whose) . . . .

. . . .

. . . .

EXERCISE C Fill in the blank in each of the following sentences with an appropriate relative pronoun. (Add 10 points for each correct answer.)

1. Aunt Martha, ... lives in Richmond, visited us last week.

2. Jeff's clown costume, ... he made, is wonderful.

3. We looked at Fred, to . . . . Mr. Acoli was pointing.

4. Marci, ... ambition is to be a forest ranger, spends her summers as a lookout in a national park.

5. Crater Lake attracts many tourists . . . . go to see the deep blue color of the lake.

6. The giant sequoia trees . . . . grow in California and Oregon are probably the tallest trees in the world.

7. The forest ranger . . . . guided us through the park told us they are sometimes 340 feet high.

8. Lori Reuter, with . . . . we traveled, took many pictures.

9. The passenger pigeon, ... was once abundant, is now extinct.

10. Mercury, ... is the smallest planet in our solar system, has craters like those on the moon.

Cumulative Review

A Circle the word or words called for in the parentheses before each sentence. (Add 4 points for each correct answer.)

(2 adjectives) A. Vacationers could see (massive) clouds in the (blue) sky.

(4 prepositions) 1. On the night of August 17, 1959, a shift in the earth's crust under the Rocky Mountains started a violent earthquake.

(subject and verb) 2. Nearly eighteen thousand visitors were staying in Yellowstone National Park that night.

(3 adverbs) 3. Fortunately, the earthquake occurred late at night, and the park roads were quite empty.

(prepositional phrase) 4. Actually, the quake also affected very large areas beyond the park.

(linking verb) 5. The damage to roads and buildings in the park was tremendous.

(direct object) 6. Rockslides had felled countless trees.

(direct object) 7. Visitors saw great fissures in the earth.

(compound verb) 8. Highways had cracked and shifted.

(2 adjectives) 9. New geysers were sending boiling mud and steam into the air.

(subject complement) 10. A few formerly active geysers suddenly became inactive.

(adverb) 11. Old Faithful, true to its name, still operated.

(4 prepositional phrases) 12. All of the trees around one pool were covered with gray mud by the eruptions.

(compound subject) 13. Rangers and other workers cleared a road for visitors to leave the park in safety.

B Indicate in the blanks at the left whether each of the following sentences is a simple sentence (*S*) or a compound sentence (*C*). Remember that a simple sentence may contain a compound subject or verb. (Add 10 points for each correct answer.)

.... 1. The eighth-graders in Ms. Meyer's class raised money and donated it to UNICEF for the holiday season.

.... 2. Each student worked in a group with two other students, and each group devised a plan for raising money.

.... 3. Denise, Elliot, and Ron ran a car wash for two weekends.

.... 4. Another group collected used books from neighbors and ran a book sale.

.... 5. Randy's group ran a pet service, and each student walked several dogs each morning before school.

.... 6. Aretha's group set up a cassette-recorder maintenance service.

.... 7. Friends would bring in their cassette recorders, and the group would service them.

.... 8. They charged fifty cents for cleaning the recorder, and the price was the best in town.

.... 9. Diane's group raised the most money.

.... 10. They ran a bicycle clinic and did all the repairs themselves.

Building Vocabulary: Getting Meaning from Prefixes

A prefix is a group of letters added to the beginning of a word. The prefix always changes the meaning of the original word.

Learn the meaning of some common prefixes.

In the following list, the prefix forms given in parentheses are used with some words to make pronunciation easier. *In*pudent and *com*fine, for example, would be hard to say. Instead, we say *im*pudent and *con*fine.

PREFIXES   in– (im–, ir–) meaning *not*
dis– (di–, dif–) meaning *away, off, down, not*
de– meaning *away, off, from, down*
com– (con–) meaning *with, together*
re– meaning *back, again*

If you can learn to recognize prefixes like these, you can often form a good guess about the meaning of words that would otherwise be new to you.

EXAMPLES   With a great effort, Herb **repressed** his urge to complain.
Your behavior, young man, has been most **irresponsible**.

In the first example, the verb *repress* is made up of the prefix *re–* plus the root *press.* You can guess that it means "to press (or hold) back." Likewise, because *irresponsible* is made up of *ir–* (*in–*) plus *responsible,* you can guess that it means "not responsible." Notice that the prefix does not usually change the part of speech of the word to which it is added.

To pin down the *whole* meaning of prefix-words like these, you should usually consult a dictionary. *Irresponsible,* for example, means more than just "not responsible." Often, it means "careless, foolish, or unfair," depending on how it is used.

EXERCISE   Using a dictionary that gives word derivations, give: (1) the prefix that is part of each italicized word and the meaning of the prefix in this word; and (2) the dictionary meaning of the word that fits the context. (Add 5 points for each correct answer.)

A. With a great effort, Herb *repressed* his urge to complain.

   (1). *re – back* ..... (2). *to hold back a desire* ....

1. The smell of the burning tire factory was extremely *disagreeable.*

   (1)................ (2)...............................

2. It was Eileen's *invariable* habit to work out in the gym each afternoon.

   (1)................ (2)...............................

67

3. Leslie should try to *conform* to our school's standards of behavior.

   (1)................ (2)...

4. The movie star insisted that it would *degrade* him to appear on the same program with a chimpanzee.

   (1)................ (2)...

5. Although everyone tried to *discredit* his story, Domenic stood firm.

   (1)................ (2)...

6. The arguments against automation are powerful but largely *irrelevant*.

   (1)................ (2)...

7. After the vacation we shall *resume* our work with new vigor.

   (1)................ (2)...

8. The man's *impudent* demands were quite rightly refused.

   (1)................ (2)...

9. As time ran out, the speaker had to *compress* her closing remarks.

   (1)................ (2)...

10. As we grow older, our first memories *recede* into the mists of time.

   (1)................ (2)...

REVIEW EXERCISE To the left of each italicized word, write the letter of its best meaning. (Add 10 points for each correct answer.)

.... 1. *assail* an enemy
.... 2. a *competent* worker
.... 3. *entice* into danger
.... 4. a *genial* companion
.... 5. the *recipient* of a medal
.... 6. receive a *reprimand*
.... 7. in the *adjacent* park
.... 8. an *auspicious* beginning
.... 9. *expire* at last
.... 10. after a lengthy *preamble*

a. to breathe out; die
b. cheerful and sympathetic
c. to attack vigorously
d. favorable, promising
e. an opening statement
f. one who receives
g. able to do what is needed
h. nearby
i. to lure
j. a strong and formal rebuke

Spelling: Four Ways to Spell /f/

Did you ever hear about the boy who spelled his dog's name *Phluphph?* This is a humorous example of the problems that arise from the many ways of spelling the consonant sound /f/ in English. George Bernard Shaw, the playwright (and a supporter of spelling reform), suggested that *ghoti* might be a logical spelling for the word *fish!* (*gh* as in *laugh; o* as in *women; ti* as in *nation.*)

Here are four ways in which the sound /f/ can be spelled in English:

f	*ff*	*ph*	*gh*
fun	cuff	phantom	cough
fuel	off	phrase	rough
leaf	cliff	telegraph	enough
beef	staff	symphony	trough

The following items contain some tips for spelling words that have the /f/ sound:

● When trying to decide whether to spell a one-syllable word like *cliff* with one *f* or two, remember that all words ending in *ff* have a *short* vowel sound preceding the *ff*'s. Therefore, you would not spell *beef* or *leaf* with two *f*'s. Why not?

● When deciding between *f* and *ph*, remember that *ph* is most commonly used in words that have a connection with science, philosophy, or some aspect of technology. The Greek language spelled the sound /f/ with *ph* (phi), and because many of our scientific and technological words are Greek in origin or use Greek word parts, we keep the Greek spelling of *ph*.

● The use of *gh* to spell the /f/ sound is unusual. It occurs at the end of only a very few words, after *ou* or *au.*

EXERCISE A Complete each unfinished word below by writing the correct spelling of the sound /f/ in the blank. (Add 10 points for each correctly spelled word.)

1. This steak is too tou . . . . to chew.

2. His navy blue jacket was covered with bits of flu . . . . from the duckling.

3. When you have a cold, you should drink a lot of . . . . luids.

4. Another word for *doctor* is . . . . ysician.

5. The ship was wrecked on a coral ree . . . .

6. "Speak right into the micro . . . . one," said the announcer.

7. When Martha saw the funny hat, she started to lau..............

8. The dog lowered its head and began to sni.............. at the meat.

9. The first paragra............ of your composition is poor.

10. The old woman's face reflected years of sorrow and grie..............

EXERCISE B Under each of the four spellings of the sound /f/ given below, fill in the blanks with words (not included in this lesson) that contain the same spelling of /f/. (Add 10 points for each correct answer.)

f	*ff*	*ph*	*gh*
....	....	....	....
....	....	....	....
....	....		

EXERCISE C Use each of the ten words you wrote for Exercise B in a separate short sentence.

1. ....
2. ....
3. ....
4. ....
5. ....
6. ....
7. ....
8. ....
9. ....
10. ....

EXERCISE D Study the spelling of all the words taught in this lesson. Be prepared to write them as your teacher dictates them. (Add 4 points for each correctly spelled word.)

REVIEW EXERCISE Be prepared to write the following words from dictation. (Add 10 points for each correctly spelled word.)

1. neigh
2. groan
3. lie
4. pain
5. glue
6. soon
7. yield
8. scheme
9. mew
10. conceited

CHAPTER FOUR

Building Sentences with Adverb Clauses

Of all the tools in ENGLISH WORKSHOP, none is more versatile than the adverb clause. Like an adjustable wrench, it can be adapted to fit an endless variety of situations. As you can guess from the name, the adverb clause is one that does the work of an adverb. Precisely because it is a clause, the adverb clause can do a great deal more than that. It is, in fact, one of the most useful devices in the language for showing, with precision, the relationships of ideas.

LESSON 36

The Adverb Clause

An adverb clause is a subordinate clause which is used as an adverb.

ADVERB	We stopped the game promptly.
ADVERB PHRASE	We stopped the game after an injury.
ADVERB CLAUSE	We stopped the game after the umpire injured a leg.

In the examples above, the words printed in red are used as adverbs to modify the verb *stopped*. All of them—adverb, adverb phrase, adverb clause—have the same function in the sentence, but the adverb clause is much more precise than the one-word adverb or the adverb phrase. The clause tells *exactly* when "we stopped the game." It can do this because it contains a subject and a verb. A prepositional phrase, of course, *never* contains a subject and a verb. This is the big difference between a phrase and a clause.

An adverb clause may tell *how, when, where, why, to what extent* (*how much* or *how long*), or *under what condition* the action of the verb is done. In the following examples, the words printed in red signal the beginning of an adverb clause. Each of the adverb clauses modifies the verb in the independent clause.

HOW	The cheerleaders yell as if victory in the game were a matter of life and death.
WHEN	My sister had long hair when she was in college.
WHERE	The jimsonweed is found wherever the soil is poor.
WHY	The children wrote on slates because paper is scarce.
HOW LONG	Mark ate until he was satisfied.
CONDITION	Unless I call you, I will take the bus from the station.

Circle the adverb clause signal in each of the following sentences. In the blank at the right, tell which question the clause answers. (Add 5 points for each correct answer.)

A. I can't go to the game (because) I have a music

lesson.   A. ...*why*....

1. He talks as if he were exhausted.   1. ....

2. Mr. Hampton won't get those apples picked unless

we help him.   2. ....

3. Let's work until we get tired.   3. ....

4. I must finish this problem before class starts. 4. ....

5. Since so many have come to help decorate for the

party, I will go home and get dressed.   5. ....

6. When those boys start singing, no one else can be

heard.   6. ....

7. Wherever Alice Yen goes, her dog follows her. 7. ....

8. We must help him because he needs our help.   8. ....

9. After we finish, we can eat.   9. ....

10. Penny acted as if nothing had happened.   10. ....

EXERCISE B   Underline the adverb clause in each of the following sentences and circle the word (or words) it modifies. Hint: In each of the following sentences, the adverb clause modifies the verb in the independent clause. (Add 10 points for each correct answer.)

A. Our class (will go) on an outing if there is enough money in the treasury.

1. We will take the trip when school is out for spring vacation.

2. We are going to the Colonial Village because the visit will help us in our

American history course.

3. Unless we collect the money soon, we may not go.

4. Our teacher will hire two buses whenever we decide on the date.

5. We will not have dinner until we get back.

Adverb Clauses and Subordinating Conjunctions

You can easily spot the difference between an adverb clause and any other group of words modifying a verb. An adverb clause must contain both a subject and a verb. An adverb phrase does not.

ADVERB PHRASE   We waited until noon.
ADVERB CLAUSE   We waited until he came.

Another way to recognize an adverb clause is to look for the word which signals the beginning of an adverb clause. You have already learned that the conjunctions *and, but, or,* and *nor* are used to join the two independent clauses in a compound sentence. There is another kind of conjunction. It joins an adverb clause to the independent clause of the sentence.

An adverb clause begins with a subordinating conjunction.

EXAMPLES   She built a fire because the cabin was cold.
We will wait until the beans are tender.
The soldiers look as though they are tired.

In the sentences above, the words printed in red are subordinating conjunctions. This kind of conjunction signals the beginning of an adverb clause and joins the clause to the rest of the sentence. Notice that a few of these words —*after, before, since,* and *until*—may also be used as prepositions.

SOME COMMON SUBORDINATING CONJUNCTIONS

HOW	as if, as though
WHEN	after, as, before, since, until, when, while
WHERE	where, wherever
WHY	because, since, so that
COMPARISON	than, as long as, as soon as
CONDITION	although, if, unless

EXERCISE A   Put parentheses around each adverb clause and underline the subordinating conjunction. (Add 5 points for each correct answer.)

A. Ricardo and Maria started swimming lessons (when they moved near the athletic club).

1. They chose this sport because they could practice it year-round.

2. They like to get in an hour of swimming before they go to school.

3. Maria concentrates on the backstroke so that she can be the best in that specialty.

4. Ricardo likes the butterfly stroke, since it develops his shoulder and arm muscles.

5. The swimmers compete in meets wherever they are held in the area.

6. If they have experience in competition, Rick and Maria will be able to swim better against other teams.

7. As they practice, Maria and Rick time themselves on each lap.

8. They analyze their performance after each meet is over.

9. Although swimming is usually an individual sport, Ricardo and Maria also swim on relay teams with other club members.

10. As soon as Maria's younger sister is old enough to compete, she will also swim on a relay team.

EXERCISE B Some of the following sentences contain adverb clauses, and some do not. If a sentence contains an adverb clause, circle the subordinating conjunction and underline the subject of the clause once and the verb twice. If the sentence does not contain a clause, write *NC* for no clause at the end of the sentence. (Add 10 points for each correctly marked sentence.)

A. Geoffrey will call me (when) he comes home.

B. I will wait until five o'clock. *NC*

1. Sometimes I can't study.

2. If you want a new coat, you should look for it now.

3. When we return home, we gather the eggs.

4. The Statue of Liberty was presented to the United States in 1884.

5. At last I was ready.

6. While we were shopping, we stopped for a soda.

7. Because I enjoy my work, I get it finished quickly.

8. At the end of the concert, the conductor bowed.

9. I have to stay in until I finish my homework.

10. Suddenly the rain started.

Placement of Adverb Clauses

You have probably noticed that adverb clauses can come at the beginning, middle, or end of a sentence. Unlike an adjective clause, which usually follows the word it modifies, an adverb clause may be moved around to suit the writer's purpose.

For variety, emphasis, and clarity, an adverb clause may be placed at various points in a sentence, often at the beginning.

EXAMPLES   Sheila broke all the balloons <u>after we had worked for hours decorating the gym.</u>

<u>After we had worked for hours decorating the gym,</u> Sheila broke all the balloons.

The second example suggests annoyance that the speaker's work has been needlessly wasted. It does this because the adverb clause is now placed where it receives greatest emphasis—at the beginning of the sentence.

For the sake of clarity, we use a comma after an introductory adverb clause—one that begins a sentence.

UNCLEAR   If a heavy fog settles traffic is slowed considerably. (Does the fog settle traffic?)

CLEAR   <u>If a heavy fog settles</u>, traffic is slowed considerably.

UNCLEAR   After we had eaten Danny arrived. (Poor Danny. Boiled or fried?)

CLEAR   <u>After we had eaten</u>, Danny arrived.

EXERCISE A   Underline the adverb clauses in the following sentences. Put a comma after any adverb clause that begins a sentence. (Add 10 points for each correctly marked sentence.)

1. When we finish studying Mom and Dad will take us to a movie.

2. The dog will come when you call.

3. While the raccoons in the cage were fighting Father got some good pictures with his movie camera.

4. My aunt put the hamburgers on the grill immediately because they had already thawed.

5. We turn down the heat whenever the radiators in our old house bang.

6. Although it is raining boys and girls in our neighborhood are playing outside in their bathing suits.

7. After the bolt of lightning struck our principal called the fire department.

8. My grandfather won't buy tickets to the World Series unless the Cardinals play.

9. Because little children can easily drown Captain Jack makes everyone wear a life jacket on the boat.

10. Since the cigarette was still smoking the ranger stepped on it to avoid the risk of fire.

EXERCISE B   The following groups of words are adverb clauses and therefore do not make full sense by themselves. Make complete sentences by adding each clause to a main statement that will give it meaning. Be sure to add a comma after an adverb clause that begins a sentence. (Add 20 points for each correct sentence.)

1. unless I study hard . . . .

. . . .

2. when the alarm sounded . . . .

. . . .

3. so that you'll learn how to swim . . . .

. . . .

4. when I finish school . . . .

. . . .

5. wherever I go . . . .

. . . .

Using Adverb Clauses

A composition in which all the sentences are choppy and repetitious is no fun to read. It probably was no fun to write, either. By using adverb clauses, we can give our writing variety, clarity, and interest.

Two independent clauses or two simple sentences may be improved by changing one of them to an adverb clause.

DULL	Alex broke his arm. *He fell out of bed.*
BETTER	Alex broke his arm when he fell out of bed.
DULL	He doesn't have to do his homework. *He has a cast on his right arm.*
BETTER	Because he has a cast on his right arm, he doesn't have to do his homework.

A compound sentence shows a relationship of some kind between the ideas expressed in the two independent clauses, but it does not always make clear just what this relationship is. We can often improve a compound sentence by changing one independent clause to an adverb clause. The adverb clause shows the relationship of the two ideas exactly.

EXAMPLES *I have started eating a nourishing breakfast,* and I feel much peppier in my early morning math class.
Since I have started eating a nourishing breakfast, I feel much peppier in my early morning math class. (The cause and effect are much clearer in this sentence.)

Frank should work as hard on science as on football, or he will be ineligible next semester.
Frank will be ineligible next semester unless he works as hard on science as he does on football. (The consequences of his lack of study are emphasized.)

EXERCISE Combine each of the following pairs of sentences into one sentence by changing the italicized sentence to an adverb clause. Use the suggested conjunction to begin the clause. Decide whether the clause sounds better at the beginning or the end of the sentence. Be sure to use a comma after an introductory adverb clause. (Add 10 points for each correct sentence.)

A. Dad called. *You were at the store.* (while) *Dad called while you were at the store.*

1. *Mother's birthday is tomorrow.* Sharon is going to bake a cake tonight.

   (because) ....

   ....

2. Art prepared the salad. *We fried the hamburgers.* (while) ....
....
....

3. I can't go to the game. *I must finish my science notebook.* (since) ...
....
....

4. *My pen ran out of ink.* I finished my outline in pencil. (after) ......
....
....

5. I worried about the history test. *I was in no danger of failing it.*
(although) ....
....

6. *We were hunting for project material.* We found three articles on swimming. (when) ....
....

7. *Pat was the smallest girl on her team.* She was the best player. (although)
....
....

8. *Brian has overslept.* He will be late for school. (since) ....
....
....

9. We gave up our picnic plans. *The rain was beginning to fall.* (because)
....
....

10. *Mother and Dad had left for the political caucus.* Alice and I began
our homework. (after) ....
....

Chapter Review

EXERCISE A   Put parentheses around the adverb clause in each of the following sentences and underline the conjunction which signals the beginning of the clause. (Add 5 points for each correct answer.)

A. Life has been very different in my family (since Mother obtained her real estate license).

1. Because she works long hours at her job, we all have additional tasks around the house.

2. Father now does most of the cooking, since he comes home first.

3. Although he cooked at barbecues and on Sunday mornings, he never before planned a weekly menu.

4. Actually he is quite a good cook although his meals sometimes lack variety.

5. He has prepared several unusual dishes because he finds them tasty.

6. Father became familiar with many exotic foods when he was a foreign correspondent for his newspaper.

7. Mother, Father, and I all pitch in and clean up after dinner, since the job gets done much quicker that way.

8. Actually we have grown closer as a family since Mother started her job.

9. We usually play Monopoly together after we have cleaned up from dinner.

10. Mother and Father are saving part of their salaries so that we can take a trip to South America this summer.

EXERCISE B   Put parentheses around the adverb clause in each of the following sentences. Underline the subject of the clause once and the verb twice. (Add 10 points for each correctly marked sentence.)

A. It seemed (as if we spent every weekend looking at houses).

1. While we were looking at one house, a girl walked over to me.

2. She acted as if she wanted a friend, too.

3. Before an hour had passed, we had become acquainted.

Underline the adverb clauses in these sentences. Put a comma after every introductory adverb clause.

4. When Andrew Jackson was thirteen he became a soldier.

5. In the Battle of New Orleans, Jackson was called "Old Hickory" by his men because he was as tough as hickory.

6. As Jackson achieved national prestige he cultivated the manners of a gentleman.

Improve each of the following pairs of sentences by changing one of the sentences into an adverb clause.

7. We are lucky to have a French girl in our class. We are studying France in social studies. . . . .

. . . .

8. She came in the middle of the year. Her father was made manager of the American branch of a French company. . . . .

. . . .

9. Colette can give us many firsthand details about life in France. We will learn much more than the facts in the book. . . . .

. . . .

10. She returns to Paris in two years. She will be able to tell French students about America. . . . .

. . . .

Cumulative Review

A Identify the italicized words in the following sentences. Write the appropriate abbreviations above each word: *n.* for *noun; pron.* for *pronoun; adj.* for *adjective; v.* for *verb; adv.* for *adverb; prep.* for *preposition; conj.* for *conjunction; int.* for *interjection.* (Add 5 points for each correct answer.)

A. *One* of the island paradises *in* the South Seas is Tahiti.

1. It *is* one of the *most* romantic *islands* in the world.

2. *It* was visited by the British naval captain, Samuel Wallis, in 1767.

3. The *magic* of Tahiti *has drawn* visitors ever since.

4. The sea *breaks* in *growling* thunder on the encircling reef.

5. The white plumes of *waterfalls* accent the steep, green *mountainsides.*

6. The Polynesian people of the island *are* extremely *handsome.*

7. Many *famous* people have visited Tahiti, *and* some have stayed *there* to live.

8. The French painter Paul Gauguin spent *many* years of his life *on* the island.

9. It *now* has an airstrip and can be visited by many tourists.

10. *My,* how I *would love* to go to Tahiti.

B Underline the items asked for in parentheses. (Add 4 points for each correct answer.)

1. Both Aldo and his brother enjoy auto racing. (compound subject, direct object, conjunction)

2. Their car, which has been adapted for stock-car racing, is quite fast. (adjective clause, subject complement, adverb)

3. Because the boys want to be safe in an emergency, they installed a shatterproof windshield. (adverb clause, direct object)

4. Aldo, who likes to tinker, is most skillful at working on the powerful engine, but his brother Sal is the more competitive driver. (simple subjects and verbs of compound sentence, adjective clause)

5. They take their car to the races which are held every Saturday. (direct

object, adjective clause, prepositional phrase)

6. Although they have not yet won a race, Aldo and Sal seem optimistic about their chances. (adverb clause, compound subject, subject complement)

7. The boys enjoy working together and want to be partners in an automotive business. (compound verb, adverb, prepositional phrase)

C Combine each of the following pairs of sentences by turning the italicized sentence into an adjective clause. (Add 20 points for each correct sentence.)

1. Mrs. Sanders enjoys gardening. *She is one of our neighbors.* . . . .
. . . .
. . . .

2. I must tell you about the great idea. *I have just thought of it.* . . . .
. . . .
. . . .

3. Cecily has a young collie. *It is the liveliest dog I have ever seen.* . . . . . .
. . . .
. . . .

4. Many mysteries were written by Doris Miles Disney. *They are both entertaining and suspenseful.* . . . .
. . . .
. . . .

5. May is coming over after supper. *I just spoke to May on the phone.* . .
. . . .
. . . .

Building Vocabulary:
Getting Meaning from Word Roots

If we take the prefix away from a word, what remains is the part of the word that carries its basic meaning. If we take the prefix *re–* from the verb *reverse,* for example, we have *verse,* which carries the basic meaning "to turn." *Reverse* must therefore mean "to turn back" (*re–*, you recall, means *back*). The basic part of this word, *–verse,* is called its *root.*

Learn the meaning of some common word roots.

Between half and two thirds of all the words in English—perhaps four hundred thousand words altogether—come to us from Latin. Most of these words of Latin origin are built up from a fairly small number of Latin word roots. In other words, if you know the basic meaning of even a few common word roots, you have a clue to the meaning of hundreds or perhaps thousands of words. Knowing the meaning of the word root can often give you the basic meaning of an unfamiliar word. It may also clarify the meaning of a word you already know (like *reverse,* above).

Here are five of the most useful Latin word roots. See how many words you can think of that contain these roots.

LATIN WORD ROOTS
-cur- (-curr-, -curs-) meaning *run, course*
-mit- (-miss-) meaning *send*
-pon- (-pos-) meaning *put, place*
-solv- (-solu-, -solut-) meaning *loosen, free*
-vert- (-vers-) meaning *turn*

Usually, these word roots are combined with prefixes to form words (*dis*miss, *re*solve). Sometimes, however, a group of letters is added to the end. A *missile,* for example, is something *sent.* A *cursory* glance at something is a *running* (hasty or superficial) glance. Although the word root can give you the basic meaning of such words, it is usually best to check this meaning in a dictionary.

EXERCISE   Each of the following verbs contains one of the Latin word roots listed above. First, draw a line between the prefix and the word root. Then give (1) the probable meaning of the word, from the meaning of the prefix and root; and (2) the meaning that you find in a dictionary. Remember that the prefixes have these meanings: *com–* (with, together); *de–* (away, down); *dis–* (away, off); *re–* (back, again). (Add 5 points for each correct answer.)

A. dis|miss   (1) *to send away* (2) *to send away or let go.*

1. compose (1)................ (2)...................................

2. concur (1)............... (2)..............................

3. convert (1)............... (2)..............................

4. depose (1)............... (2)..............................

5. dissolve (1)............... (2)..............................

6. divert (1)............... (2)..............................

7. recur (1)............... (2)..............................

8. remit (1)............... (2)..............................

9. repose (1)............... (2)..............................

10. revert (1)............... (2)..............................

REVIEW EXERCISE Fill each blank with the word from the following list that makes the best sense in the context. (Add 10 points for each correct answer.)

compress heretic   irrelevant resume   smug   tantalize
discredit impudent   recede   secluded subtle vigilance

1. The lawyer tried to .... the witness on the ground that he was a habitual liar.

2. His arguments were too .... for the children to follow.

3. Joan of Arc was considered a(n) .... during her lifetime.

4. The smells of dinner cooking in the kitchen .... us while we wait for it to be served.

5. We chose a(n) .... spot for our campsite at some distance from the road and the other campers.

6. Gradually, the runners' hopes of winning the race ...., and they want only to be able to finish.

7. An encyclopedia may .... into a single article information gathered from hundreds of books.

8. Only by constant .... did Lee manage to keep his canoe from overturning in the rapids.

9. Don't let yourself become .... merely because you have given a few right answers.

10. The .... student ran into me, knocked my books on the ground, and then expected *me* to apologize.

Spelling:
Adding Suffixes to Words Ending in Silent *e*

Adding suffixes to words that end in silent *e* can cause spelling problems. Sometimes the silent *e* is dropped, and sometimes it is retained. Study the two columns of words below and see if you can work out two general rules for adding suffixes to words that end in silent *e*.

1	2
peace + ful = peaceful	divide + ing = dividing
value + less = valueless	surprise + ed = surprised
polite + ness = politeness	rehearse + al = rehearsal
arrange + ment = arrangement	advise + able = advisable
lone + ly = lonely	continue + ous = continuous

Here is the first rule.

Drop the final silent *e* when adding a suffix that begins with a vowel.

EXCEPTIONS Words that end in *ce* or *ge* usually *keep* the final silent *e* before the suffixes *–able* and *–ous*. The silent *e* is necessary to keep the sound of *c* and *g* "soft."

noticeable   courageous
enforceable   outrageous

How would the word *noticeable* be pronounced if the final *e* in the base word *notice* were dropped? Say the word. Now try saying the word *courageous*, omitting the final silent *e* from the base word *courage*.

Here is the second rule.

Keep the final silent *e* when adding a suffix that begins with a consonant.

EXCEPTIONS argument truly judgment

EXERCISE A Join each base word and its suffix to form a new word. Write the new word in the blank. Keep in mind the two rules you have been studying. (Add 5 points for each correctly spelled word.)

1. waste + ful = ...

2. sense + less = ...

3. desire + able = ...

4. separate + ing = ...

5. insure + ance = ...

6. true + ly = ...

7. store + age = ...

8. argue + ment = ...

9. decide + ed = ...

10. advantage + ous = ...

11. nature + al = ...

12. sincere + ity = ...

13. attractive + ness = ...

14. adventure + ous = ...

15. change + able = ...

16. refine + ment = ...

17. guide + ance = ...

18. immediate + ly = ...

19. nine + ty = ...

20. judge + ment = ...

EXERCISE B   Write five example words (other than those given in this lesson) for each of the two general rules you have studied. (Add 10 points for each correct answer.)

FIRST RULE	SECOND RULE
1.	6. ....
2.	7. ....
3.	8. ....
4.	9. ....
5.	10. ....

EXERCISE C   Study all the words taught in this lesson, and be prepared to write them from dictation.

REVIEW EXERCISE   Be prepared to write the following words from dictation. (Add 10 points for each correctly spelled word.)

1. beef
2. fuel
3. paragraph
4. cliff
5. cough
6. fluff
7. symphony
8. phrase
9. leaf
10. enough

CHAPTER FIVE

Punctuation

In conversation, an expression like "you're going home" can be a statement, a question, or an exclamation, depending on how it is said. In speaking, you use your voice to show how your words fit together in sentences and to make your meaning clear in many other ways. In writing, however, you do not have these voice signals to clarify meaning. Instead, you must use various marks of punctuation, which you shall study in this chapter.

LESSON 44

End Marks:
Period, Question Mark, Exclamation Point

A statement is followed by a period (.).

EXAMPLES   We saw the remains of an old stone wall in the woods.
Perhaps the land had once been a farm.

A question is followed by a question mark (?).

EXAMPLES   Has this land belonged to your family for a long time?
Do you often play in the woods?

An exclamation is followed by an exclamation point (!).

EXAMPLES   What fun it is to explore in a place like this!
Look, there goes a rabbit!

An imperative (command) sentence is followed by either a period or an exclamation point.

If the command shows strong feeling, an exclamation point is used. A command which does not show strong feeling is followed by a period.

EXAMPLES   Watch out!
Please hand me the binoculars.

Caution: Do not overuse the exclamation mark. Merely adding it to a statement does not always turn the statement into a real exclamation. Often a change in wording is also necessary.

EXERCISE A   Add an appropriate end mark to each of the following sentences. (Add 10 points for each correctly marked sentence.)

1. Mr. Appleton is very much interested in the past

2. Is that why he bought the old Hertzog house

3. He has spent hours in the courthouse looking up old records

4. What an interesting pastime that must be

5. It is interesting if history fascinates you

6. Does Mr. Appleton have a regular job

7. No, he is retired and has taken up local history as a hobby

8. Would he be angry if I asked him about the woods

9. Ring his doorbell and find out

10. Mr. Appleton came originally from Columbia, Missouri

EXERCISE B   Some of the sentences below are statements and some are questions. Change the statements to questions and the questions to statements, adding the appropriate end marks to the new sentences and making such changes in wording as you need to. (Add 20 points for each correct sentence.)

A. The fire engines are coming. ... *Are the fire engines coming?* ....

1. Is someone going to repair this typewriter? ....

2. Did you say the beach is two miles from here? ....

3. You will write the report tomorrow. ....

4. Were you waiting to see me, young man? ....

5. Does the line reach the end of the block? ....

Commas to Separate Words and Phrases

Use commas to separate words, phrases, or subordinate clauses written in a series.

A *series* is three or more of the same kind of sentence parts which follow one after the other.

WORDS IN SERIES   Geysers are found in America, Iceland, and New. Zealand.

PHRASES IN SERIES   I looked for my shoes in my closet, under my bed, and behind my desk.

CLAUSES IN SERIES   We wondered who the man was, why he had come, and what he was trying to do.

A comma is sometimes needed to separate two or more adjectives modifying the same noun.

EXAMPLES   The boys were wearing baggy, long-sleeved sweaters.
Elephants are lazy, friendly, and good-natured.

Do not use a comma between the final adjective and the noun it modifies.

INCORRECT   Sandra saw a large, ugly, gull.
CORRECT   Sandra saw a large, ugly gull.

In some cases a final adjective is so closely related to a noun that they almost form one expression.

EXAMPLE   Sandra saw a gray sea gull. (*Sea gull* is one expression. There is no comma between *gray* and *sea gull*.)

Use a comma after an adverb clause or a long phrase that begins a sentence.

A clause or phrase that begins a sentence is called an *introductory* clause or phrase. An introductory adverb clause is always separated from the rest of the sentence by a comma. Two short prepositional phrases or one long one also requires a comma for clarity. A single short phrase, however, is usually clear without a comma.

ADVERB CLAUSE   After we eat, we shall do the dishes.
TWO PHRASES   After the last concert in the park, we had a picnic.
SHORT PHRASE   After lunch we will go to the beach. (no comma)

EXERCISE A Punctuate the following sentences with commas where necessary. (Add 10 points for each correctly marked sentence.)

1. Mrs. Jones stopped her car opened the door and walked to a telephone booth near the roadside.

2. For lunch we had soup salad and delicious banana bread.

3. When we leave where we'll go and how long we'll stay are problems yet to be settled.

4. Dr. Solomon ordered hot applications liniment and rest for my foot.

5. I soaked my foot rubbed it and walked very little for several days.

6. Orange juice cereal lettuce meat and vegetables are on the grocery list.

7. After a hot muggy afternoon we had a violent thunderstorm.

8. As long as you plan to go downtown will you pick up a train schedule at the station for me?

9. The Salt Lake City weather bureau announced that we have had the coldest winter since 1897.

10. The hound chased the rabbit across the meadow through the swamp and into the woods.

EXERCISE B Clarify these sentences by inserting the necessary commas between adjectives modifying the same noun. (Add 10 points for each correctly marked sentence.)

1. The long dark pathway led to a grim ruined house.

2. The movie was advertised as gigantic stupendous and colossal.

3. All seventh-grade eighth-grade and ninth-grade boys should report to the gym.

4. The snowstorm, with its enormous white drifting flakes, was beautiful.

5. Skating hockey and skiing are Marcia's favorite sports.

6. The past three Saturdays have been windy cold and rainy.

7. We saw the hunters come back with a huge mountain lion.

8. Coretta is knitting a red ski hat for her boyfriend.

9. Our lunchroom is too often hot crowded noisy and littered.

10. I am looking for a pair of black fur-lined gloves.

Commas for Interrupters

We often interrupt what we are saying with a word or phrase that is not essential to our main thought. In conversation we show that such expressions are *interrupters* by a change of voice. In writing we accomplish the same thing by means of punctuation.

Use commas to set off expressions that interrupt the sentence.

There are four main kinds of interrupters: introductory words, parenthetical expressions, appositives, and words of direct address.

1. Introductory Words An introductory word helps get a statement started. Because it can generally be omitted without changing the meaning of a sentence, it is set off by a comma.

EXAMPLES Well, shall we go?
No, I do not think so.
Actually, we were planning to come.

2. Parenthetical Expressions An interrupting word or comment is set off by commas because it is not necessary to the meaning of the sentence. Such expressions may occur at the beginning or end of a sentence, or in the middle.

EXAMPLES Leopards, for example, are still found in India.
That will not be necessary, in my opinion.
However, I thought the book was too easy.

3. Appositives An appositive is a word which means the same thing as the word it follows and explains it in some way. It may have modifiers. An *appositive phrase* is an appositive plus its modifiers.

EXAMPLES This is Mrs. Clark, the president of the bank.
Skiing, my favorite sport, is quite easy to learn.

4. Words of Direct Address A word of direct address names the person to whom we are speaking. In writing it occurs mainly in quoted conversation.

EXAMPLES Will you help me, John?
Helen, your friends are here.
Now, my friends, you will see a feat of magic.

Add commas where they are necessary in the following sentences. (Add 10 points for each correctly marked sentence.)

A. Burt, have you ever met Dr. Stearns?

1. Dr. Stearns our new neighbor is a veterinarian.

2. She has a marvelous gift with animals I'm sure.

3. For example even a gentle dog will bite when it is hurt.

4. The sickest dog seems to know however that Dr. Stearns is its friend.

5. Not long ago a strange dog was run over by a delivery truck on Carter Drive a street near the doctor's house.

6. Well Dr. Stearns ran out of the house when she heard the noise.

7. "Can you do anything Doc?" someone asked.

8. The dog a big yellow mongrel let her come near without a growl.

9. She took care of the dog for quite a while three months altogether.

10. She did not of course expect to be paid for what she did.

EXERCISE B Rewrite the following sentences, adding to each the kind of interrupter specified. Use commas wherever necessary. (Add 20 points for each correct sentence.)

A. I enjoy watching baseball.   (appositive)

 I enjoy watching baseball, a fine spectator sport.

1. I am glad that you came.   (introductory word)

 . . . .

2. You are too late to go on the tour.   (word of direct address)

 . . . .

3. This tour is the one that goes to New York City.   (appositive)

 . . . .

 . . . .

4. You may go on the next tour.   (parenthetical expression)

 . . . .

5. My best friend is coming with us.   (appositive)

 . . . .

Commas for Dates and Addresses

In a date or address consisting of two or more parts, put a comma after each part.

The parts of a date may include: the time of day; the day of the week; the day of the month; and the year. In the following example, vertical lines separate the four parts of the date.

EXAMPLE   8 P.M. | Saturday | September 27 | 1981

When we use any two (or more) of these parts to express time, we set them off by commas.

COMMAS NEEDED   On November 9, 1976, Dr. Adams joined the expedition.

The polls open at 6 o'clock, Saturday, May 2, at Willow Run School.

NO COMMAS   On June 5 we begin our vacation.

The parts of an address may include: the street number and street; the apartment number; the city; the state; and the zip code. (There is *never* a comma between the state and the zip code.)

EXAMPLE   201 Dexter Avenue | Apartment 2B | Macon | Georgia 31204

Again, any two (or more) of these parts used in an address must be set off by commas.

COMMAS NEEDED   Mamie has lived in Sycamore, Illinois, since 1975.

Benedict Carter's new address is 2345 Beverly Road, Apartment 3D, Brooklyn, New York 11223.

NO COMMAS   We moved to Tulsa two years ago.

EXERCISE A   Punctuate the following dates and addresses as if they were included in sentences by putting a *comma after each part*. Do not use commas for dates and addresses consisting of only one part. (Add 5 points for each correctly marked sentence.)

A. before Sunday, March 5,

1. at 3 P.M. Monday February 7 1983

2. from February 1 to February 5 1823

3. at 757 Third Avenue New York New York 10017 U.S.A.

4. on the corner of Fifth Avenue and Fiftieth Street New York City

5. on Friday April 3 and Saturday April 4

93

6. from Apartment 7W

7. near Pittsburgh Pennsylvania

8. at Evanston Township High School Evanston Illinois

9. to 2107 Carney Avenue Baltimore Maryland 21234

10. soon after 5 o'clock Tuesday June 24 1980

11. next Tuesday June 23

12. from 1776 Ashland Circle Boise Idaho 83705

13. on the afternoon of Friday August 31

14. next Friday afternoon

15. at 221B Baker Street London N.W.1 England

16. in the city of San Francisco

17. at 85 Sheridan Avenue Ho-Ho-Kus New Jersey 07643

18. in the year 1776

19. located at Green Acres Shopping Center Sunrise Highway Valley Stream New York

20. until November 17 1982

EXERCISE B   Insert the commas that are missing from the following paragraph. (Add 10 points for each correct answer.)

1   My grandfather on my father's side was born in Calhoun County
2   South Carolina on March 2 1898. He grew up in a house at 1716 Cedar
3   Street Weldon North Carolina, in the northern part of the state. As a
4   girl, Grandma lived just around the corner from him, at 210 East Sixth
5   Street. She was several years younger than he, however, and he never
6   noticed her until September 1917 when he went off to war with the
7   Weldon volunteers. They were married soon after Christmas the same
8   year, on Saturday December 27, 1917. They moved to Texas soon after
9   Grandpa got out of the army in 1919. They have lived in the same house
10 ever since, at 3 Park Terrace Houston Texas 77017.

Apostrophes Show Possession

One of the main uses of the apostrophe is to help a noun to show possession. The placement of the apostrophe depends on whether the noun is *singular* (referring to only one person or thing) or *plural* (referring to more than one).

To form the possessive of a singular noun, add an apostrophe s ('s).

EXAMPLES   a bride's gown   a mouse's tail
                 Donna's reply   Charles's hat

Notice that the apostrophe is attached only to the possessive noun, not to the noun that is possessed.

INCORRECT   a student's friend's   a reporter's source's
CORRECT   a student's friends   a reporter's sources

To form the possessive of a plural noun which does not end in s, add an apostrophe s ('s).

EXAMPLES   children's toys   mice's tails
                 women's choices   geese's wings

To form the possessive of a plural noun ending in s, add only the apostrophe (').

EXAMPLES   our friends' homes   the dogs' collars
                 the students' bicycles   the babies' playpens

Apostrophes are *never* used with the following possessive pronouns:

NO APOSTROPHE   his   theirs   its   whose
                      hers   ours   yours

EXERCISE A   In the first blank, write the singular possessive form of the numbered word. In the second blank, write the plural possessive form of the same word. Make sure the placement of your apostrophe is clear. (Add 5 points for each correct answer.)

	Singular		Plural	
A. teacher	*teacher's*	desk	*teachers'*	desks
1. dog	. . . .	tail	. . . .	tails
2. son	. . . .	smile	. . . .	smiles

	Singular		Plural
3. cat	. . . . eyes		. . . . eyes
4. sister	. . . . task		. . . . tasks
5. detective	. . . . question		. . . . questions
6. mouse	. . . . squeak		. . . . squeaks
7. doctor	. . . . car		. . . . cars
8. neighbor	. . . . yard		. . . . yards
9. baby	. . . . bottle		. . . . bottles
10. house	. . . . chimney		. . . . chimneys

EXERCISE B   Add apostrophes where they are necessary in the following sentences. (Add 5 points for each correctly marked sentence.)

A. The deer's coat was speckled with sunlight.

1. Lorettas and Pauls papers are on Miss Conways desk, but ours aren't.

2. One of the boys had lost his fathers jacket.

3. What shall we do with the geeses feathers?

4. In the Middle Ages a gooses feathers were used in arrows.

5. A pelicans beak is more than a foot long, and its neck has a kink in it.

6. Our grandparents old schoolbooks look dull compared with todays.

7. Please tell me the companys address.

8. What have they predicted for tomorrows weather?

9. He is so quick that he does about eight hours work in three hours.

10. Our towns oldest house is out on the river road.

11. My oldest brothers pet mice are as big as yours.

12. There are two mens overalls hanging behind the barn door.

13. Marie didn't give the problem a moments thought.

14. The mayors friends formed a citizens committee to reelect her.

15. Have you seen todays papers anywhere?

16. Raymonds bicycle is in better condition than yours.

17. Someone left the dogs leash on the front porch.

18. The childrens toys were scattered behind the sofa.

19. Our citys tallest buildings have all been built recently.

20. The twins mother has won an award for her story.

96

Apostrophes for Contractions

A contraction is a word made by combining or shortening two words.

Use an apostrophe to show where letters have been omitted in a contraction.

EXAMPLES   You'll (you will) be late if you don't (do not) hurry.

The apostrophe in a contraction goes in where the letters have come out.

EXAMPLES   have not = haven't   I am = I'm   who is = who's

When *not* is contracted (*n't*), be careful to put the apostrophe between the *n* and *t* where the *o* is omitted.

INCORRECT   does'nt   do'nt   should'nt
CORRECT   doesn't   don't   shouldn't

EXERCISE A   Write out the two words for which each contraction stands. (Add 4 points for each correct item.)

1. you're......................   6. isn't ....

2. she'd......................   7. we're ....

3. can't......................   8. hasn't ....

4. wasn't......................   9. he'll ....

5. don't ....   10. you'll ....

Write the contraction for each of the following.

11. it is......................   16. he would ....

12. are not......................   17. let us ....

13. she will ....   18. where is ....

14. there is......................   19. I will ....

15. they are ....   20. we would......................

After each sentence write the contraction which may be used in place of the italicized words.

21. *We had* hoped to leave by now. ....

22. *It will* turn out all right. ....

23. John *is not* late today. ....

24. *It is* only eight o'clock. ....

25. *You had* better hurry. ....

Do not confuse contractions with the possessive pronouns that sound like them.

EXAMPLES They're (they are) not here.
They left their books.

You're (you are) right.
Take your coat.

It's (it is) late.
Its color is fading.

Who's (who is) ready to go?
Whose sweater is this?

When in doubt about whether a word is a contraction, think of the words that the contraction is shortening.

EXERCISE B Underline the correct word in the parentheses. (Add 10 points for each correct answer.)

A. Al, here is (you're, your) pencil.

1. Does that tree shed (it's, its) leaves?

2. Both men think (they're, their) going to win that golf match.

3. They have started (they're, their) game.

4. (Who's, Whose) voice do I hear?

5. Are you the one (who's, whose) singing?

6. (It's, Its) time to go home.

7. (You're, Your) the only one who can beat me in badminton.

8. May I borrow (you're, your) sweater?

9. (It's, Its) becoming quite chilly.

10. The explorers have lost (they're, their) way.

Punctuating Quotations

Quotations are the exact words written or spoken by someone and reported by someone else. We need to know how to punctuate quotations if we want to report what people said in a real situation or if we are writing a story in which people talk to each other.

Use quotation marks (" ") to enclose a direct quotation—a person's exact words. A direct quotation begins with a capital letter and is set off from the rest of the sentence by commas.

EXAMPLE "My aunt lives in Puerto Rico," said Elena. She added, "I may visit her next summer."

If you wanted to tell what Elena said without using her exact words, you would use an *indirect quotation.* Indirect quotations do not require quotation marks.

EXAMPLE Elena said that her aunt lives in Puerto Rico. She added that she may visit her aunt next summer.

A period or a comma following a quotation should be placed inside the closing quotation marks (," or .").

EXAMPLES "I am sure I took my key," said Terry.
John spoke up, "You manage to lose everything."

If the quotation is a question or exclamation, a question mark or an exclamation point should be placed inside the closing quotation marks (?" or !"). If the entire sentence is a question or an exclamation, a question mark or exclamation point should come after the quotation marks ("? or "!).

EXAMPLES "Come down off that ladder!" shouted Mr. Papalou. (The exclamation point is inside the quotation marks because the quotation is an exclamation.)
"Is the fudge cool enough to eat?" asked Grandfather. (The question mark is inside the quotation marks because the quotation is a question.)
What a fool he was to say, "You're welcome"! (The quotation is not an exclamation. The exclamation point is outside the quotation marks because it applies to the whole sentence, not just to the quotation.)
What begins, "Down in the valley"? (The quotation is not a question. The question mark is outside the quotation marks because it applies to the whole sentence, not to the quotation.)

EXERCISE A   Add capitals and punctuation marks (including end marks, commas, and quotation marks) where needed in the following sentences. (Add 10 points for each correctly marked sentence.)

A.   "I just saw my favorite movie on television," said Caroline.

1. What was it asked Gary

2. It was *The Maltese Falcon* with Humphrey Bogart replied Caroline

3. Oh, I love that film exclaimed Bernice

4. Is that the movie about Sam Spade, the private eye asked Gary

5. Bernice said I like the character of Brigit O'Shaunessey best

6. I like comedies better than mysteries replied Gary

7. Do you have a favorite movie asked Caroline

8. I think *The African Queen* with Katharine Hepburn is my favorite responded Gary

9. Did you see *Gone with the Wind* on television inquired Caroline

10. That is my favorite movie of all time said Bernice

EXERCISE B   Follow the same directions for the conversation below. (Add 10 points for each correctly marked sentence.)

1. Are you going to try out for the school play asked Dawn

2. I would love to be in it, but I'm afraid I would freeze once I was out on the stage said Connie

3. That is all the more reason for auditioning replied Dawn

4. You have to face your fears in order to conquer them said Ernesto

5. You would be perfect for the role of Sabina in *The Skin of Our Teeth* responded Dawn

6. That's the role I wanted said Connie

7. Ernesto, are you going to audition for the role of Mr. Anthropus inquired Dawn

8. I sure am exclaimed Ernesto

9. Wow, that's great because I'm trying out for the part of Mrs. Anthropus exclaimed Dawn

10. Then we may all be in the play together said Connie

Punctuating Longer Quotations

The part of the sentence that tells who is speaking sometimes interrupts a quotation in the middle.

When a quoted sentence is divided into two parts by an interrupting expression such as he said or Mother asked, the second part of the quotation begins with a small letter.

EXAMPLE   "This old box," said Mr. Sims, "was buried under the rocks."

The exceptions to this rule are the personal pronoun *I* and proper nouns, which are always capitalized wherever they appear in a sentence.

EXAMPLES   "In spite of the rain," Armand said, "I am going to the game."
"I think," he added, "John is going too."

When you write dialogue (two or more persons having a conversation), begin a new paragraph each time the speaker changes.

EXAMPLE   "Does anyone want to go to the game tonight?" asked Father, peering over the evening paper.
"I'd like to go," answered Edward. "I think our team will win."
"According to the paper, our team has a good chance of winning the series," added Janice.
"Let's all go!" exclaimed Mother.

When a quotation consists of several sentences, put quotation marks only at the beginning and at the end of the whole quotation, not around each sentence in the quotation.

EXAMPLE   "Good afternoon, future scientists and normal people," the speaker began. We all laughed. "Your principal has asked me to tell you a little about the career opportunities in science. (*no quotation marks*) There are many different kinds of jobs available. (*no quotation marks*) You can work in research, development, production, sales, or teaching and still be a scientist."

EXERCISE A   Punctuate the following sentences of dialogue. Use quotation marks, commas, and end marks. When you find a place where a new paragraph is required, identify it with this sign, ¶. (Add 4 points for each correct answer.)

1 I propose that we take a canoe trip down the Delaware said Larry
2 with enthusiasm. We could rent the canoes in Callicoon and paddle down
3 to Bingham Falls he added. I think that's a good idea said Charlotte
4 but how do we get the canoes back to Callicoon. That's easy said Larry.
5 There is a series of posts along the river where you can leave the canoes.
6 You rent them at one post and check them in at a post farther down
7 the river Larry added. Should we schedule the trip for next week asked
8 Bruce.

EXERCISE B Correct the following sentences. Cross out any incorrect punctuation and capitals and add any punctuation marks or capital letters that have been omitted. (Add 10 points for each correctly marked sentence.)

1. About how long a trip will it be, asked Charlotte.

2. It's about twelve miles, replied Larry, "so we shall have to prepare for the trip lasting all day."

3. "We'll need two adults to come with us, commented Sharon, since they will have to rent the canoes and provide supervision."

4. Ms. Roth, the supervisor of the Canoe Club, replied "I, of course, shall be glad to come." "Mr. Spenser, the mathematics teacher, canoed down that part of the river last year, so perhaps he could come with us too."

5. Shall we ask Mr. Spenser to come with us asked Annette, the club secretary?"

6. That sounds like a good idea, said Ms. Roth, "And I'll personally ask him to come."

7. "We should make a map of the area, said Eugene. We could indicate where to expect white water."

8. Charlotte added "we could also show points along the land bordering the river that would help us know where we are.

9. "We could arrange for a speaker to talk to the club about handling a canoe in white water suggested Ms. Roth.

10. My parents are excellent canoeists, said Eugene and I'm sure they would be glad to come to talk to us."

Chapter Review

EXERCISE A Correct the punctuation of the following passage by adding commas, quotation marks, end marks, apostrophes, and capital letters where they are needed. Draw a line (/) through any incorrect punctuation you find and correct it. (Add 2 points for each correct answer.)

1   It was a dry hot sunny, day. At the end of our first week in Arizona

2   we were going to a rodeo. As we arrived Robin wanted to know if thered

3   be a steer-roping contest.

4   Yes said Dad And youll see some bareback, bronco riding too.

5   Robin can just anyone enter that calf-riding contest that you men-

6   tioned asked Brian.

7   Youve got to be under twelve Robin replied also you have to have

8   your parents permission before you can enter

9   Folks may I ride in the contest Brian immediately asked?

10   Why of course you may they answered Well even come and watch

11   you.

12   Swell said Brian Where do I register

EXERCISE B Add commas to the following dates and addresses as you would if they were in the middle of a sentence. (Add 20 points for each correctly marked item.)

1. on Thursday January 13 1983 at 2 P.M.

2. since Friday July 11 1980

3. around five o'clock on November 11 1981

4. to 597 Ives Avenue Flint Michigan 48506

5. not far from Rensselaer Avenue Albany New York

EXERCISE C In the space after each word, write the possessive form of the word. (Add 10 points for each correct answer.)

1. boy ....   4. books ....   7. poet ....

2. men ....   5. oxen ....   8. children ....

3. persons ....   6. moose ....   9. animals ....

                                                10. year ....

Cumulative Review

A Underline the word or words asked for in parentheses. (Add 10 points for each correct answer.)

1. Audrey's suitcase had been checked, and the airline tickets were safely in her wallet.   (2 simple subjects and 2 complete verbs)

2. She was dressed neatly in a turtleneck sweater and jeans.   (prepositional phrase)

3. She was making her first jet flight alone.   (direct object)

4. Audrey felt nervous when the plane took off.   (subject complement)

5. The captain announced that they would probably be late.   (1 adverb and 1 adjective)

6. As soon as the plane halted, she dashed out and ran.   (compound verb)

B Underline the adjective clause in each sentence and circle the word it modifies. (Add 20 points for each correctly marked sentence.)

1. Her connecting flight, which was on another airline, was about to take off.

2. Finally she spotted the gate, which was closed.

3. She opened it and saw the plane, which was beginning to move.

4. She waved frantically at the faces that were in the windows.

5. The copilot, who saw her coming, halted the plane.

C Put parentheses around the adverb clause in each sentence, and underline the subject of the clause once and the verb of the clause twice. (Add 20 points for each correctly marked sentence.)

1. After she had caught her breath, the other passengers asked her about her mad dash.

2. She would have plenty to talk about when she got home.

3. "If I make another trip, I'll plan it better," she said.

4. It was after eleven before the plane landed.

5. As Audrey stepped from the plane, she waved excitedly.

Building Vocabulary: Getting Meaning from Suffixes

Whether you know it or not, you are acquainted with quite a number of word families. Consider the *child* family, for example. If you add *–ish* to this word, you have an adjective, *childish,* which means "like a child." In turn, you can make an adverb out of *childish* by adding *–ly: childishly,* meaning "in a childish manner." And what is *childishness?* The *–ness* ending tells us that the noun *childishness* means "the state or quality of being childish."

These word endings added to *child* to make up the *child* family of words are called *suffixes.* Notice that each suffix goes with a particular part of speech and changes the meaning of the root word in a definite way. If we can recognize suffixes in words and know their meaning, we have a key to the meanings of whole families of words.

Learn the meaning of some common suffixes.

ADJECTIVE SUFFIXES	–able (–ible) meaning *able, fit, likely*
	–ful meaning *full of, marked by*
	–ive meaning *tending to, marked by*
NOUN SUFFIXES	–tion (–ion) meaning *action, state, result*
	–ty meaning *quality, state*

Let's see how some of these suffixes work. Here, for example, are words made by adding some of them to the verb *exclude,* which means "to keep out."

ADJECTIVES	Certain kinds of income are exclud<u>able</u> for income tax purposes.
	Mr. Garcia has joined a very exclus<u>ive</u> club.
NOUN	The exclu<u>sion</u> of spelling from the test was a relief to everyone.

Even without the help of context, we can form a good idea of the meaning of the underlined words if we learn the meaning of the suffixes. *Excludable* would mean "fit to be excluded (kept out)." *Exclusive* would mean "tending to exclude." *Exclusion* would be the "act or result of excluding." Notice that the spelling of the root word may change when a suffix is added. Nevertheless, it is still easy to see where the original word ends and the suffix begins.

EXERCISE A Using a dictionary, write the noun or adjective form as indicated for each italicized word. Each adjective or noun is to be formed by adding one of the suffixes listed in this lesson. Be sure that you spell each new word correctly. (Add 10 points for each correct answer.)

	Noun	*Adjective*	*Adjective*
compel	A. compulsion	B. compellable	C. compulsive
bliss		1.	
stable	2.		
fret		3.	
speculate	4.	5.	
inoculate	6.	7.	
perceive	8.	9.	10. ....

EXERCISE B To the left of each sentence, write the letter of the best meaning for the italicized word. (Add 10 points for each correct answer.)

a. Extremely happy; joyous.
b. Firmness, steadiness.
c. Worried and peevish.
d. The act of thinking about the various aspects of something without reaching a final conclusion; also, an opinion reached by this kind of thinking, a theory or guess.
e. Of an idea or opinion, theoretical, not final; of a business venture, risky.
f. The act of putting into the body a substance that will prevent a specific disease; also, the substance given for this purpose.
g. The act of gaining knowledge of an object by means of the senses, by seeing, hearing, etc.; also, the ability to do this or the knowledge of an object gained in this way.
h. Capable of being known, or noticed, by any of the senses, especially the sense of sight.
i. Having the power to gain knowledge by observation; quick in understanding, keen.
j. The act of forcing someone to do something; also, a state of mind in which one feels a necessity to do something.

.... 1. We spent a *blissful* /blís fəl/ summer at Camp Winnebago.

.... 2. After seeing the Olympic Games, Gary developed a *compulsion* /kəm púl shən/ for physical fitness.

.... 3. The baby was hungry and had become rather *fretful* /frét fəl/.

.... 4. Anyone entering the United States must show proof of *inoculation* /in ók yə lá shən/ against smallpox.

.... 5. In the fog, the road was barely *perceptible* /pər sép tə bəl/.

.... 6. Two persons' *perception* /pər sép shən/ of the same thing may differ greatly.

.... 7. Georgia's discussion of the poem was very *perceptive* /pər sép tiv/.

.... 8. There has been much *speculation* /spék yə lá shən/ about the possibility of intelligent life on other planets.

.... 9. My suggestion was purely *speculative* /spék yə lá tiv/.

.... 10. The Swiss government is noted for its *stability* /stə bíl ə tē/.

Spelling: Two Rules for the Unruly Final *y*

In George Washington's time, people had several ways of spelling a word ending in *y* to which they wanted to add a suffix. Washington himself, when writing about both East New Jersey and West New Jersey, alternated between the spellings *Jerseys* and *Jersies*. Today, however, there are rules that govern what is done with a final *y* before a suffix is added. If you learn these rules, along with an example or two for each, your spelling can be free of errors involving the final *y*. Look at how the following base words with final *y* are spelled when various endings (or suffixes) are added. Besides ending in *y*, what else do all of the base words have in common?

1	*2*
obey + s = obeys	gray + er = grayer
joy + ful = joyful	gay + est = gayest
money + less = moneyless	annoy + ed = annoyed
employ + ment = employment	buy + ing = buying

None of the base words changed when endings (or suffixes) were added. This is true whether the suffix begins with a consonant or a vowel. The endings added in column 1 all begin with a consonant; those in column 2 with a vowel. *All* the base words have this in common: the final *y* is preceded by a vowel.

When final *y* is preceded by a vowel, do *not* change the *y*; simply add the ending.

EXCEPTION   daily (day + ly)

1	*2*	*3*
silly + ness = silliness	copy + es = copies	try + ing = trying
beauty + ful = beautiful	reply + ed = replied	hurry + ing = hurrying
merry + ment = merriment	early + er = earlier	forty + ish = fortyish
happy + ly = happily	lazy + est = laziest	hobby + ist = hobbyist

When final *y* is preceded by a consonant, change the *y* to *i* before adding any suffix, *except* a suffix beginning with *i*. With *i*, keep the *y*.

EXERCISE A   Join each base word and its ending (suffix) to form a new word. Write the new word in the blank. Apply the two rules you have learned. (Add 5 points for each correctly spelled word.)

1. cry + es = ...   4. display + s = ...

2. joy + ful = ...   5. hilly + ness = ...

3. pity + ful = ...   6. coy + ness = ...

7. repay + ment = ...   14. destroy + ing = ...

8. weary + ed = ...   15. satisfactory + ly = ...

9. play + er = ...   16. carry + ing = ...

10. happy + est = ...   17. multiply + ing = ...

11. baby + ish = ...   18. accompany + ment = ...

12. greedy + est = ...   19. lobby + ist = ...

13. delay + ed = ...   20. busy + er = ...

EXERCISE B   Fill in the blank in each word below with *i* or *y*, whichever is correct. (Add 10 points for each correct answer.)

1. heart....ly   6. carr....ing

2. haz....er   7. plent....ful

3. empt....ed   8. ceremon....es

4. enjo....ing   9. fur....ous

5. embod....ment   10. sevent....ish

EXERCISE C   Write four words (other than those taught) that illustrate the two rules in this lesson. First write the base word, then the suffix, and finally the new word itself. Use a different suffix for each word. Words 1 and 2 should illustrate the first rule; words 3 and 4, the second. (Add 25 points for each correctly spelled word.)

	BASE WORD	+	SUFFIX	=	NEW WORD
1.	....	+	....	=	....
2.	....	+	....	=	....
3.	....	+	....	=	....
4.	....	+	....	=	....

REVIEW EXERCISE   Be prepared to write the following words from dictation. (Add 10 points for each correctly spelled word.)

1. storage   6. judgment

2. valueless   7. lonely

3. advisable   8. arrangement

4. truly   9. enforceable

5. outrageous   10. adventurous

THE PARTS OF SPEECH Identify the italicized words by writing one of the following abbreviations above each word: *n.* (noun), *pron.* (pronoun), *v.* (verb), *adj.* (adjective), *adv.* (adverb), *prep.* (preposition), *conj.* (conjunction), *inter.* (interjection). (Add 5 points for each correct answer.)

1   My brother has played the flute *for* many years. He has always played

2   in the orchestra and has enjoyed *it* very much. I thought he would *lose*

3   interest in the instrument once he was in high school, but he has a

4   *wonderful* teacher, who gives *him* pieces to learn that will hold his

5   interest. Mr. Harris told him about the role of the flute in Latin American

6   music and brought *some* interesting *records* for him to hear. *Dwight* is

7   now learning to play salsa on his flute *and* has joined a group at school

8   that *plays* for dances. His next ambition is to learn the piccolo, which is

9   *important* in any marching *band.* This instrument, a *shrill* cousin *of* the

10   flute, will make it possible for Dwight to march in parades and see all the

11   *football* games. Music has brought *my* brother much enjoyment. I *am*

12   eager to learn to play an instrument, and I *hope* to be a musician like my

13   brother. I'd *like* to take piano lessons. *Oh,* what fun it will be.

THE PARTS OF A SENTENCE Find the subjects and verbs in the following sentences. Underline the subjects once and the verbs twice. Watch out for sentences with compound subjects and verbs and note any compound sentences. (Add 5 points for each correct sentence.)

1. Judy and I were sitting on the front steps of her house the other day and were complaining about our dull existence.

2. Nothing exciting ever happens around our neighborhood.

3. Suddenly we heard the long wail of a siren, and it came closer and closer.

4. Then the fire engine rushed down the street with its bell clanging.

5. Both of us looked for the fire.

6. A column of smoke rose from the vacant lot on the corner.

7. Some children had been playing with matches, and the grass was burning.

8. The firefighters put out the blaze in a hurry.

9. They had almost a hundred spectators in a few minutes.

10. Neither of us would want that kind of excitement again.

The following sentences contain prepositional phrases, direct objects, and subject complements. Underline the part of the sentence asked for in parentheses.

11. Animals are beloved characters in many books. (subj. complement)

12. Walter Farley has written many books about horses. (prep. phrase)

13. As a boy Farley kept notes about horses. (direct object)

14. Later he used these notes in his books. (prep. phrase)

15. Farley became the owner of a horse farm. (subj. complement)

16. Kathryn Cook was also a lover of horses. (prep. phrase)

17. "Ba-ee" is the name of a story by Kathryn Cook. (subj. complement)

18. As a child Doris Gates wanted a burro. (direct object)

19. At last she had one of her own. (direct object)

20. The burro became the inspiration for a book. (subj. complement)

THE ADJECTIVE CLAUSE Underline the adjective clause in each sentence and circle the word it modifies. (Add 10 points for each correct sentence.)

1. Hildegarde Hawthorne wrote a biography of her famous grandfather, who was Nathaniel Hawthorne.

2. Hawthorne was a writer who took pains to write with great care and thought.

3. Hawthorne was a classmate of Longfellow, whom we all know as the author of *Hiawatha* and *Evangeline*.

4. Dr. Conally, who was a close friend of Hawthorne, told the writer the story of a young Acadian girl.

5. Hawthorne, who liked the story, never used it.

6. Longfellow, who knew the tale, asked permission many years later to use the story as the basis for a poem.

7. The poem is *Evangeline,* which is one of America's best-loved works of literature.

Combine the pairs of sentences below into single sentences by making the italicized sentence into an adjective clause.

8. Emily Dickinson is more famous now than many writers who were popular in her day. *She never allowed her poems to be published.* ...

. . . .

. . . .

. . . .

9. One of Mark Twain's most famous stories is "The Celebrated Jumping Frog of Calaveras County." *It is a tall tale in the frontier tradition* ...

. . . .

. . . .

. . . .

10. Gwendolyn Brooks has received several awards and honors for her poetry. *She began putting rhymes together when she was seven years old.*

. . . .

. . . .

. . . .

THE ADVERB CLAUSE Put parentheses around the adverb clause in each sentence. Underline the subject of the clause once and the verb twice. (Add 10 points for each correctly marked sentence.)

A. (Because my father has taught medicine for many years,) he knows doctors all over the world.

1. One of his friends must live in Nigeria because she is the head of a hospital there.

2. When she has leave in the United States, she sometimes comes to visit us.

3. Since she tells fascinating tales about Africa, we all love to have her come.

4. Once, a dangerous and at the same time very funny situation arose while she and some friends were sitting down to dinner.

5. As someone was proposing a toast, a column of army ants came through the door.

6. Wherever army ants appear, they eat everything in their path.

7. You must get out of the way if you value your life.

8. All climbed on the dining table so that they might be safe.

9. Table legs are set in kerosene whenever these insects are a menace.

10. The family dog, the guests, and the roast beef spent the afternoon on the table while the ants worked their way through the house.

PUNCTUATION Punctuate the following sentences by adding quotation marks, commas, apostrophes, and end marks wherever necessary. (Add 10 points for each correctly marked sentence.)

1. Watch out shouted the man in the car Cant you see Im signaling for a turn

2. Mr. Abernathy sent us a postcard a piece of petrified wood and a souvenir of Seattle Washington while he was on his vacation.

3. Well why dont you look in the boys gym suggested Mr. Fidducci Ill bet youll find Jacks sweatshirt there

4. Because we have moved recently our mail is being forwarded from 234 Knox Circle Evanston Illinois 60201 to 4080 River Drive in Charleston South Carolina.

5. The Drama Clubs production of *Abe Lincoln in Illinois* will be presented on Friday night June 1 in the auditorium.

6. Baseball swimming and hiking are Selmas favorite summer activities.

7. Mr. O'Malley our science teacher is planning an exhibit of student drawings reports and projects.

8. Have you seen my copy of *The Red Pony* Sarah she asked I thought Id left it in Joans room

9. On Friday January 11 1980 Tina was fourteen years old

10. Although Tony is pretty good he isnt the teams best pitcher said Paul This years award in my opinion should go to either Ossie or Larry he continued

CHAPTER SIX

Fragments and Run-ons

When it comes to writing clear, informative sentences, too much is just as bad as not enough. When two sentences are run together as if they were one, the writer has made the mistake of "too much"—the *run-on sentence*. When a part of a sentence is chopped off and written as if it were a sentence, the writer has made the mistake of "too little"—the *sentence fragment*. You can avoid both kinds of mistakes if your sentence sense is working properly. That is what we shall be concerned with in this chapter.

LESSON 56

Sentence Fragments

A complete sentence has a subject and a verb and expresses a complete thought. It makes sense by itself.

A sentence fragment is a separated part of a sentence that does not express a complete thought.

FRAGMENT Which you visited last year. (*What* did you visit last year? This is not a complete thought.)

SENTENCE We stayed at Yellowstone Park, which you visited last year.

FRAGMENT After the testimonial dinner at the club. (This has no subject or verb. It does not make sense by itself.)

SENTENCE After the testimonial dinner at the club, many guests told stories of the doctor's kindness.

FRAGMENT And lost his gloves on the way home. (This fragment has a verb but no subject. It is really half a compound predicate and needs the rest of the sentence to make sense.)

SENTENCE Matthew left his books at school and lost his gloves on the way home.

In order to make sure you have written a sentence and not a sentence fragment, ask yourself these questions: Does it have a subject and a verb? Does it express a complete thought? If a word group does not meet both of these requirements, it is a fragment and not a sentence.

EXERCISE Write *S* before each group of words that is a sentence. Begin the sentence with a capital letter and end it with a period. Write *F* before each group of words that is a fragment. (Add 4 points for each correctly marked item.) *F*

S.. A. fishing is Kevin's favorite hobby.

F.. B. especially in salt water

.... 1. because so many different kinds of fish

.... 2. Kevin has several rods and reels

.... 3. the bluefish start running in the late summer

.... 4. traveling in schools and feeding greedily

.... 5. they require big hooks and a strong rod

.... 6. striped bass also good to eat

.... 7. they breed in freshwater rivers

.... 8. return to the ocean during adulthood

.... 9. also big tuna off Block Island

.... 10. party boats take many people to the fishing grounds

.... 11. flounder can be found in coves

.... 12. pull your hook up a couple of inches from the bottom

.... 13. excellent to pan-fry for supper

.... 14. some fish are not good to eat

.... 15. menhaden are caught for fertilizer

.... 16. a sea trout caught off the end of the pier

.... 17. out in the rowboat at dawn

.... 18. sandworms make very good bait

.... 19. a funny-looking fish is the sea robin

.... 20. it swells up to twice its size when caught

.... 21. designed to frighten its enemies

.... 22. a good scaling knife and a board to put the fish on

.... 23. one time Kevin caught an eel

.... 24. threw him back into the water

.... 25. nothing better than good, fresh fish

Clause Fragments

You might have recognized some of the sentence fragments in the last lesson as subordinate clauses. Although a subordinate clause has a subject and a verb, it is not a sentence because it does not express a complete thought.

A subordinate clause must not be written as a sentence.

FRAGMENTS   if I win the class election
which we found in the attic
because we had not eaten much breakfast

Each of these fragments is a clause that must be attached to a main statement. Note how each clause (underscored in red) depends for its meaning on the main statement.

SENTENCES   I'll keep my promises <u>if I win the class election</u>.
My parents enjoy the old records <u>which we found in the attic</u>.
<u>Because we had not eaten much breakfast</u>, we were starved by noon.

When a clause follows the main statement of a sentence, some people make the mistake of putting a period at the end of the main statement, thus separating it from the clause. This makes a fragment out of the clause.

FRAGMENT   It was nine o'clock, *When I finished my homework.*
SENTENCE   It was nine o'clock <u>when I finished my homework</u>.

FRAGMENT   I watched television for a half hour, *Before I went to bed.*
SENTENCE   I watched television for a half hour <u>before I went to bed</u>.

Adding a subordinating conjunction to a sentence changes the sentence to a fragment.

SENTENCE   I need a new coat.
FRAGMENT   *Because* I need a new coat (What about it?)

EXERCISE A   In the following groups of words, write *S* before each group that is a sentence and end the sentence with a period. Write *F* before each group that is a fragment. (Add 10 points for each correctly marked item.)

.... 1. The summit of Mount Everest in the Himalayas is the highest point on earth

.... 2. Because Tenzing Norgay had always wanted to climb Mount Everest

.... 3. Tenzing devoted his life to the dream of reaching the top of the great mountain

115

.... 4. In May, 1953, while Tenzing was on an expedition with some British climbers

.... 5. With Edmund P. Hillary he formed one of the climbing teams

.... 6. Which they succeeded in reaching on May 29, 1953

.... 7. This unknown Sherpa guide who started the dangerous climb with Hillary

.... 8. After his successful climb had made him famous

.... 9. Because his people have no written language, Tenzing could not write his own story

.... 10. Then James Ullman talked with Tenzing and wrote *Tiger of the Snows* for him

EXERCISE B   Add each clause fragment to an independent clause, which you will supply, so that the result will be a complete sentence. (Add 20 points for each correct sentence.)

1. whenever I go to school in the rain ....

....

....

2. if you would read this book about Helen Keller ....

....

....

3. as if I had all the time in the world ....

....

....

4. which we thought we had finished ....

....

....

5. whose dog I had found ....

....

....

116

Phrase Fragments

A phrase is a group of words that is used in the same way as a single part of speech—a one-word modifier. Because a phrase can consist of several words and may express an important idea, careless writers may separate it with a period and a capital letter from the sentence in which it belongs. A phrase cannot stand alone as a separate sentence because it does not have a subject and a verb and does not express a complete thought.

A phrase must be clearly connected with the word it modifies. It must not be written as a sentence.

FRAGMENT   Our newspapers carry news items, *From all over.* (The italicized phrase is a prepositional phrase modifying the word *items.* It cannot be a separate sentence.)

SENTENCE   Our newspapers carry news items <u>from all over</u>.

FRAGMENT   I worked hard, *Cleaning my room.* (*Cleaning my room* is another kind of phrase, based on the *–ing* (or *–ed*) form of a verb. It has no subject and no complete verb.)

SENTENCE   I worked hard <u>cleaning my room</u>.

FRAGMENT   Father will not throw away his old straw hat, *Purchased in Bermuda seven years ago.*

SENTENCE   Father will not throw away his old straw hat, <u>purchased in Bermuda seven years ago</u>.

FRAGMENT   In 1588 King Philip II of Spain brought together one hundred and fifty ships, *A huge fleet for those times.* (The italicized phrase is an appositive phrase. It cannot be a separate sentence.)

SENTENCE   In 1588 King Philip II of Spain brought together one hundred and fifty ships, <u>a huge fleet for those times</u>.

In order to make sense, a phrase must be clearly connected to the word it modifies. Just as a one-word modifier cannot be written as a separate sentence, a phrase cannot stand alone as a sentence either.

EXERCISE Some of the following word groups contain two sentences. Others contain a sentence and a sentence fragment. Write *S* if both are sentences. Write *F* if one is a fragment, and correct the sentence fragment by changing the punctuation and joining it to the rest of the sentence. (Add 10 points for each correctly marked item.)

F. A. Gordon Parks gained fame as a photographer in the late 1930's, *a*
After years of hardship and discouragement.

.... 1. Many people enjoy taking pictures. They use them as a record of family events.

.... 2. Photography is often used to record public events. This use of photography is called photojournalism.

.... 3. A photograph can also be a work of art. Exhibiting the same beauty of composition as a fine painting.

.... 4. Karsch of Ottawa takes portraits of famous people. These portraits reveal their subjects' characters.

.... 5. Margaret Bourke-White was one of the first women to become famous as a photographer. She took excellent news photos.

.... 6. Ansel Adams is well known for his landscape photographs. Especially those of mountain scenery.

.... 7. A remarkable book of photographs is called *The Family of Man*. It shows people from all over the world.

.... 8. Advertising photography can be an interesting career. One which requires skill and imagination.

.... 9. It is possible to combine photography with other special interests. For example, zoology or mineralogy.

.... 10. Camera manufacturers are constantly making it easier for photography fans. They make cameras more automatic.

Correcting Sentence Fragments

EXERCISE A   Each of the numbered items below consists of two groups of words. If both are sentences, write *S* in front of the number. If one is a sentence fragment, write *F* and correct the mistake. (Add 5 points for each correctly marked item.)

. . . .   1. The land that is now Georgia was once inhabited by the Cherokees. Who were a southern branch of the Iroquois.

. . . .   2. They built rectangular houses with curved roofs. Covered with thatch and bark.

. . . .   3. Around their towns they built palisades. Which are fences of stakes set firmly in the ground.

. . . .   4. They constructed their towns in fortified places in the mountains. So that they could live in peace from aggressive neighbors.

. . . .   5. As more and more settlers moved to the area. Conflict developed between the way of life of the Cherokees and that of the new inhabitants.

. . . .   6. The Cherokees tried to adapt to the new culture. When the settlers moved into their lands.

. . . .   7. Under the leadership of Chief Sequoya, they drew up a constitution for their nation. Following the example of the settlers.

. . . .   8. Chief Sequoya invented the Cherokee alphabet. We still have copies of songs written by the Cherokees in their alphabet.

. . . .   9. Some Cherokees attempted to keep records of their rituals and activities. So that their culture could be preserved.

. . . .   10. Many people consider Chief Sequoya a great man. His name has been given to the huge, strong trees that grow in California.

. . . .   11. Many of the new settlers did not want to live side by side with the Cherokees. Whom they considered a conquered nation.

. . . .   12. Some Cherokee farmers were very prosperous. Their new neighbors longed for their possessions.

.... 13. In 1802 the federal government agreed to move the Cherokees from Georgia. They were promised land in the Great Plains.

.... 14. In 1829 gold was discovered in Dahlonega, Georgia. Which made the settlers even more eager to move the Cherokees.

.... 15. The Cherokees tried to obtain justice. And brought suit against Georgia.

.... 16. At first the Supreme Court refused to hear the case. Which was called "Cherokee Nation v. Georgia, 1831."

.... 17. Finally the Court was forced to take the case. It upheld the rights of the Cherokees.

.... 18. It seemed like a victory. Except that the President refused to intervene when Georgia denied the Cherokees their rights.

.... 19. Finally the Cherokees were forced to leave their ancestral home. In favor of lands promised them in the Great Plains.

.... 20. Many suffered and died during the journey to the new territory. The trail they followed came to be known as the "trail of tears."

EXERCISE B   Attach the sentence fragments in the paragraph below to the sentences with which they belong. Cross out the incorrect periods and capital letters. Add commas where needed. (Add 20 points for each correctly marked sentence.)

STARS AND STRIPES

1   Today, there are still only thirteen stripes in the American flag, but
2   there might have been fifty. If Congress had not changed its mind. On
3   January 1, 1776, General Washington flew the first flag of the United
4   States. The Grand Union flag. It had two crosses with a stripe. For each
5   of the original thirteen colonies. In 1777 Congress changed the flag. By
6   adding a blue field with thirteen stars. As new states entered the Union.
7   Stars and stripes were added, until in 1818 Congress restored the original
8   thirteen stripes.

Run-on Sentences

A run-on sentence, like a sentence fragment, is an error made because a writer fails to recognize the sentence as a unit. A run-on sentence is really two or more sentences run together or separated only by a comma.

A sentence should be followed by a period, a question mark, or an exclamation point. Do not use a comma between sentences.

RUN-ON   The Panama Canal has been of great value, it links both our coasts by water.

SENTENCE   The Panama Canal has been of great value. It links both our coasts by water.

RUN-ON   Mike has a snare drum, he takes lessons on it.

SENTENCE   Mike has a snare drum. He takes lessons on it.

RUN-ON   What was all the trouble about, she knew she had done nothing wrong.

SENTENCE   What was all the trouble about? She knew she had done nothing wrong.

Then and *it* are two "dangerous words" often used to tie two sentences together, making them a run-on sentence.

RUN-ON   Roberta tied her shoelaces, then she ran back onto the field.

SENTENCE   Roberta tied her shoelaces. Then she ran back onto the field.

RUN-ON   I enjoyed the movie Saturday night, it was a musical starring Liza Minelli.

SENTENCE   I enjoyed the movie Saturday night. It was a musical starring Liza Minelli.

EXERCISE A   Write *R* if the numbered word group contains a run-on sentence. Correct the run-on sentence by capitalizing and punctuating it as two separate sentences. Write *S* if the numbered group is one sentence. (Add 10 points for each correctly marked item.)

_R_. A. Each year thousands of Americans visit Canada, some have summer homes near Canada's beautiful lakes and rivers.

_S_. B. Because it is such a vast country, Canada offers a wide range of tourist attractions.

.... 1. The St. Lawrence Seaway opened the Great Lakes to large ocean vessels, a cruise up the seaway makes a pleasant vacation.

.... 2. Travelers may also take boat trips from Seattle to Victoria, then they can go on to Vancouver from Victoria.

.... 3. By shopping in Victoria and Vancouver, tourists can find their favorite British products.

.... 4. Fine bone china cups and saucers are available, collecting these is a hobby for many people.

.... 5. A popular resort area is Banff and Lake Louise, a region of great beauty.

.... 6. A trip through the Canadian Rockies is memorable, many of the rugged mountains are covered with snow all summer.

.... 7. Churchill, near Hudson Bay, is the gateway to the Far North.

.... 8. The Calgary Stampede is a popular attraction, it features bareback riders.

.... 9. The Canadian side of Niagara Falls is beautiful, you can go right up to the Horseshoe Falls.

.... 10. A trip to Ottawa should include a visit to the stately buildings of Canada's Parliament, they are built in the Gothic style.

EXERCISE B   Identify each of the following sentences as compound (*C*), run-on (*R*), or simple (*S*). (Add 25 points for each correctly marked sentence.)

.... 1. Robert Ettiger is the founder of the cryonics movement.

.... 2. Believers in the movement are frozen upon death, and their bodies are kept in special temperature-controlled units.

.... 3. Scientists may eventually find cures for all terminal diseases, patients "in cryonic suspension" will then be brought back to life.

.... 4. Woody Allen once wrote a script for a movie about this topic, the movie was called *Sleeper* and starred Diane Keaton.

More Practice with Run-on Sentences

EXERCISE A Correct the run-on sentences in the following paragraphs by inserting periods and capital letters where needed. Be careful not to produce any sentence fragments. (Add 10 points for each corrected run-on sentence.)

WEATHER WISDOM, THEN AND NOW

1   Today, when they forecast the weather, modern meteorologists can
2   count on the help of an impressive battery of scientific devices. Weather
3   satellites, for example, relay photographs of cloud formations from all
4   over the world, these pictures show where storms are beginning over
5   oceans and deserts, the paths of typhoons and hurricanes are tracked
6   in the same way. Weather information from all sources is fed into
7   electronic computers, in this way it can be evaluated with amazing
8   rapidity.

9   Our ancestors had no complicated weather instruments, they had to
10 rely on their eyes and ears and a few old proverbs and maxims. Their
11 methods were hardly scientific, however, some were founded on fact.
12 Today, for example, no one still believes the old superstition about the
13 groundhog, but we celebrate Groundhog Day just the same. If the
14 groundhog saw its shadow on February second, there were supposed
15 to be six more weeks of winter, try it yourself and see! The behavior
16 of insects, on the other hand, is still a good indicator of temperature,
17 the reason is that they are coldblooded. Grasshoppers cannot fly when
18 the temperature goes below 55 degrees Fahrenheit if you hear a
19 cricket chirping, count the number of chirps in fourteen seconds and
20 add forty, then you will have the temperature in degrees Fahrenheit.

21   Weather forecasting is more accurate, if less picturesque, than it was
22 in the old days, however, the forecasters still seem to be as often right
23 as wrong, perhaps because there are so many factors to consider.

123

EXERCISE B   Identify each of the following as a run-on sentence (*R*), a compound sentence (*C*), or a simple sentence (*S*). Correct each of the run-on sentences by supplying a capital letter and a period. (Add 10 points for each correctly marked item.)

....   1. A tide is a rising and falling of a body of water, it is caused by the moon's pull on the earth's surface.

....   2. The tides vary according to the phases of the moon, the highest tides come at the full moon and in the dark of the moon.

....   3. The highest tide of the month is called the *perigee tide*.

....   4. The Bay of Fundy on the eastern coast of Canada has the highest tides in the world, they rise over fifty feet in many parts of the bay.

....   5. The Bay of Fundy also has a tidal bore, it comes in all at once like a wave or a wall of water.

....   6. The fantastic tides in the Bay of Fundy are due to the long and narrow shape of the bay.

....   7. Some places in Alaska have thirty-foot tides, and it looks very strange at low tide to see a large ship sitting on the mud.

....   8. On straight coastlines near the continental shelf, the difference between high and low tide is much less.

....   9. Most places have two high tides and two low tides every twenty-five hours, but there are some coasts with only one of each.

.... 10. Ships usually leave and enter harbors at high tide, it is therefore necessary to predict when the high tide will occur.

Chapter Review

EXERCISE A Identify each of the following as a complete sentence (*S*), a sentence fragment (*F*), or a run-on sentence (*R*). (Add 5 points for each correct answer.)

.... 1. Langston Hughes was born in Joplin, Missouri, he grew up in Lawrence, Kansas and Cleveland, Ohio.

.... 2. After more than a year at sea as a sailor aboard a freighter.

.... 3. Working in Paris as a cook.

.... 4. When he returned to the United States, he went to Washington and worked in a hotel.

.... 5. Hughes struggled to support himself, his main ambition was to be a writer.

.... 6. Vachel Lindsay, a famous poet, stayed at the hotel where Hughes was working, and Hughes showed him some of his poetry.

.... 7. Lindsay was very enthusiastic about Hughes's poetry, he wanted to present some of it at a public reading he was giving of his own work.

.... 8. Thrilled by the enthusiasm and support of this famous poet.

.... 9. After the reading, critics gave good reviews to the work of the new poet.

.... 10. Moved to New York City where he became one of the Harlem Renaissance writers.

.... 11. In 1925 Hughes won first prize in a poetry contest, he published his first book of poetry the next year.

.... 12. It was called *The Weary Blues.*

.... 13. In his poetry Hughes sought to capture the rhythms of jazz and of Black dialect.

.... 14. Realizing the importance of a better education.

.... 15. Hughes resumed his work on a degree at Lincoln University, he graduated in 1929.

.... 16. By the time he graduated from college.

.... 17. He had written his first novel and had won the Witter Bynner Prize for poetry.

.... 18. The novel was published in 1930, it was called *Not Without Laughter.*

.... 19. At the time of his death in 1967, he had obtained an international reputation.

.... 20. His works included novels, short stories, biographies, children's books, translations, opera librettos, and poetry.

EXERCISE B   Use capitals and periods to show where each sentence begins and ends. (Add 10 points for each correction in sentence division.)

A GREAT AMERICAN POET

1   Most of us take a long time to discover what we want to be others are
2   luckier and find their vocations early in life the famous poet Gwendolyn
3   Brooks started writing when she was ten by the time she was thirteen, her
4   poems were appearing in children's magazines as she matured as an
5   artist, she sought to translate her experiences growing up in Chicago's
6   South Side community into literature her poems deal with the joys and
7   sorrows of the lives of the people in the community the poems portray
8   the frustrations these people suffered in 1945 Gwendolyn Brooks pub-
9   lished her first collection of poetry, *A Street in Bronzeville* for her second
10   collection, *Annie Allen,* she was awarded the Pulitzer Prize she was the
11   first Black American to obtain this distinction among her other works is
12   *Maud Martha,* which is a story of her childhood.

Cumulative Review

A Above each italicized word write its part of speech, using the abbreviations below. (Add 4 points for each correct answer.)

n. for *noun*	*adv.* for *adverb*
pron. for *pronoun*	*prep.* for *preposition*
adj. for *adjective*	*conj.* for *conjunction*
v. for *verb*	*int.* for *interjection*

A BRAVE HISTORIAN

1   The lives of *those* who have overcome great obstacles are an inspira-

2 tion to me, *and* the writer and explorer Francis Parkman is among my

3 *special* heroes. His own life, it *seems* to me, is *more* admirable in many

4 ways than the *lives* of the famous people he wrote *about. Its outstanding*

5 quality was *courage.*

In the following paragraph, show how the italicized words are used by writing one of these abbreviations above each word: *subj.* for *subject; v.* for *verb* (including helpers); *d.o.* for *direct object;* and *s.c.* for *subject complement.*

6   In spite of his adventurous life, *Parkman* was not a healthy *person.*

7 He was nearly blind. In his later years, *arthritis* crippled his *hands,*

8 making it impossible for him to write. No *handicap* could stop *him.* He

9 spent painful *hours* studying the documents on which the accuracy of

10 his writings depended. He *hired secretaries* and *learned* to dictate his

11 books to them. After graduating from college, he lived with the Sioux,

12 who taught *him* to hunt buffalo and antelope as they did. With them

13 *he* fought bravely against their traditional enemies, the Snake tribe.

14 *Research provided* the facts for Parkman's books, but their vivid *excite-*

15 *ment* grew out of his own experiences.

B Underline each subordinate clause in these sentences. In the blank at the right of the sentence, write *adj.* if it is an adjective clause and *adv.* if it is an adverb clause. (Add 10 points for each correctly marked sentence.)

1. Sandy McGovern owns a dog whose name is Business.   1. . . . . . .

2. Business is a dog that always looks busy.   2. . . . . . .

127

3. It got its name because it trots along the street in a very businesslike fashion.

4. Perhaps it is going to a meeting at which several other dogs are planning an attack on a cat or a garbage can.

    3. . . . . . .
    4. . . . . . .

5. Business also tries to boss the members of the McGovern family, who, in its opinion, are incapable of running their own lives.

    5. . . . . . .

6. It wakes Sandy at seven o'clock every morning whether it is a school day or not.

    6. . . . . . .

7. It leads little Nancy McGovern home by the hand whenever in its opinion she is getting too far away.

    7. . . . . . .

8. The McGoverns appreciate this because it keeps Nancy out of the street.

    8. . . . . . .

9. I have heard of several dogs that behaved like people.

    9. . . . . . .

10. Business is the most amusing animal that I have ever seen.

    10. . . . . . .

C Add end marks, commas, apostrophes, and quotation marks wherever they are needed in these sentences. (Add 20 points for each correctly marked sentence.)

1. Watch out! Heres the train Stan said

2. Stand back on the platform shouted the stationmaster

3. What train is this asked the man with the big suitcase. Is it the express from Richmond

4. No the stationmaster explained the Richmond train was held up by switch trouble in Washington.

5. Oh, no exclaimed the man. Ill miss my connection in Florence South Carolina

Building Vocabulary: Choosing the Right Word

Using words is a little like shooting at a target. People with good vocabularies hit the bull's-eye of meaning almost every time. Other people fire off whole swarms of words in their efforts to say what they mean, and it's purely accidental if they ever hit the target. A few people's word marksmanship is so poor that they're a positive menace to have around.

Choose the word that says precisely what you want to say.

English is so rich a language that for anything you try to say there are usually several possible words with more or less similar meanings. Suppose, for example, that you are trying to tell how your throat feels after having your tonsils out. The pain is so great that you can hardly stand it—you just have to do something about it. What would you say?

EXAMPLE   The pain was (troublesome, annoying, intolerable).

For the meaning suggested above, *intolerable* would be the best choice. From the prefix and suffix, you know that it means "not capable of being tolerated (borne, put up with)." *Intolerable* is a strong word. Not many things are intolerable, but when they are, it is useful to know the word that says precisely how we feel about them.

Often a single, well-chosen word can replace a whole phrase. The precise word will usually be clearer and more forceful than the phrase.

WORDY   The snow *reflected* the sunlight *in many small flashes.*
PRECISE   The snow sparkled in the sunlight.

EXERCISE   Each italicized word or word group can be replaced by a single, more precise word from the list of words defined on the following page. Study each context carefully. Then read the definitions and decide which word fits. Cross out the italicized word or word group and write the replacement above it. (Add 10 points for each correct answer.)

1. The ranger's *loneliness* was extreme in winter, when the nearest town was ten miles away by dogsled.

2. The senator's *high and mighty* attitude toward working people caused him to lose the election.

3. The children were, in fact, merely *rude,* but they thought they were being very funny when they barged into the meeting.

4. Students who hadn't done their assignments were enough to *annoy beyond endurance* the bad-tempered Mr. Miller.

5. As she remembered how soon the summer would be over, a *sad* expression came over Cybel's face.

6. A small amount of salt is *necessary* to human health.

7. Professor Gloria O'Keefe, who lived in Tahiti for ten years, has a *personal* knowledge of the customs of the South Sea islanders.

8. My parents would often *scold* me *openly and critically* for being so slow to get up in the morning.

9. It is foolish to *guess* what people are really like based solely on their appearance.

10. Some toothpastes advertise that if you use them, you will become *mysteriously attractive*.

alluring /ə lóor ing/, *adj.* Arousing interest and leading on to something not clearly seen or understood.

chide /chīd/, *v.* To find fault with; to scold or criticize severely.

exasperate /ig zás pə rāt/, *v.* To make people exceedingly angry, especially by provoking them time and again.

impertinent /im púr tə nənt/, *adj.* Offensively bold; offensive to one's sense of proper behavior.

indispensable /in dis pén sə bəl/, *adj.* Impossible to do without.

intimate /ín tə mit/, *adj.* Deeply familiar through close contact.

isolation /ī sə lā́ shən/, *n.* The state of being cut off from contact with others.

lofty /laúf tē/, *adj.* Very proud, from a feeling of one's own refinement and worthiness.

surmise /sər mī́z/, *v.* To form a judgment from very slight evidence, with the help of imagination or suspicion.

wistful /wíst fəl/, *adj.* Longing for something, but with little hope of getting it; thoughtful and vaguely unhappy.

REVIEW EXERCISE   To the left of each italicized word in the left-hand column, write the letter of the best meaning. (Add 10 points for each correct answer.)

.... 1. a *disagreeable* smell

.... 2. his *invariable* custom

.... 3. *dissolve* a meeting

.... 4. *divert* one's attention

.... 5. *depose* a monarch

.... 6. events sometimes *recur*

.... 7. a *blissful* marriage

.... 8. not without *compulsion*

.... 9. a *perceptive* teacher

.... 10. the ship's *stability*

a. unchanging

b. to turn away, distract

c. the use of force

d. unpleasant

e. to put down, overthrow

f. to break up, separate

g. keenly observant, quick

h. extremely happy

i. steadiness, firmness

j. to happen again

130

Spelling: Doubling Final Consonants in One-Syllable Words

Have you ever, when you wanted to write the past tense of such words as *tap* or *pin*, ended up writing *taped* and *pined* instead of *tapped* and *pinned*? How can you know whether or not to double the final consonant in such words? There is a sound clue in each of these words that can help you to avoid misspellings of this kind. What do the vowels (printed in red) of the words listed in column *1* below have in common? What do those in column *2* have in common?

	1	*2*
	plan	plane
	rob	robe
	grip	gripe

The vowels printed in red in the first column all have a short sound; those in the second, a long one. How can you tell that those in column *2* have a long sound? The final silent *e* in each word is your clue. You know that a final silent *e* coming after a single consonant preceded by a single vowel makes that vowel long. Because the words in column *1* do *not* end in silent *e* but in a single consonant, you know that the vowel is short.

Now see how the short vowel sound of the words in column *1* is preserved when a suffix beginning with a vowel is added to each:

plan + ed = pla**nn**ed   rob + ing = ro**bb**ing   grip + er = gri**pp**er

If you do *not* double the final consonant, you lose the short sound of the vowel and get three entirely different words, each with a *long* vowel sound: *planed, robed, griper.* Why?

Here is a rule that will help you to spell words such as those in column *1* when you want to add an ending that begins with a vowel:

When a one-syllable word ends in a single consonant preceded by a single vowel, usually double the final consonant before adding a suffix that begins with a vowel.

EXERCISE A In the blank, write a word that rhymes with the word given. (Add 10 points for each correct answer.)

EXAMPLE dropping ....*shopping*.

1. hopped ....

2. bidding ....

3. knitter ....

4. dimmest......................

5. scrubbing ....   8. dining ....

6. moped ....   9. matter ....

7. fibbed ....   10. ruder ....

EXERCISE B   Join each base word below with its suffix. Write the new word in the blank. Remember to listen for the sound of the vowel in each base word and new word. (Add 10 points for each correctly spelled word.)

1. cane + ing = ...   6. sad + en = ...

2. sin + er = ...   7. slope + ed = ...

3. slim + est = ...   8. red + ish = ...

4. lop + ed = ...   9. cube + ed = ...

5. tube + ing = ...   10. web + ing = ...

EXERCISE C   In the sentences below, cross out any of the italicized words that do not make sense. Rewrite each incorrect word, correctly spelled, in the blank. If an italicized word is correct, write *C* in the blank. (Add 20 points for each correct answer.)

1. I expect to see Leon *latter* on today. ....

2. "You are *fated* to stardom," recited the actor. ....

3. We went horseback *ridding* this noon. ....

4. Someone was *taping* at the window. ....

5. Don't be so *hoggish* about your food! ....

EXERCISE D   Use any four words you made in Exercise B in separate short sentences. (Add 25 points for each correct sentence.)

1. ....

2. ....

3. ....

4. ....

REVIEW EXERCISE   Be prepared to write the following words from dictation. (Add 10 points for each correctly spelled word.)

1. silliness   6. hobbyist
2. joyful   7. beautiful
3. satisfactorily   8. buying
4. accompaniment   9. replied
5. fortyish   10. daily

CHAPTER SEVEN

Using Capital Letters

Because a capital letter is larger than other letters, it calls attention to any word with which it is used. We capitalize the initial letter of words that are important and warrant attention. A failure to do so could result in confusion. The rules for capitalization which you will study in this chapter should leave you in no doubt about when to use the capital letters and when *not* to use them.

LESSON 66

Proper Nouns

A proper noun is the name of a particular person, place, or thing. A proper noun begins with a capital letter. A common noun does not.

PROPER NOUNS	COMMON NOUNS
Ella Grasso	governor
Philadelphia	city
Redwood Highway	road
Mongolian	race
Buddhism	religion

Capitalize the names of particular persons, places, races, and religions.

PERSONS	Pablo Casals, Albert Einstein, Jane Addams, Maya Angelou
PLACES	North America, Lake Tahoe, Minnesota, Seventh Avenue
RACES	Mongolian, Polynesian
RELIGIONS	Christianity, Hinduism, Catholicism, Judaism

A word like *lake, street, city,* or *river* is capitalized only when it is part of a proper noun. Words such as *southwest, north,* and *east* are capitalized only when they refer to geographical regions, not when they indicate directions.

PROPER NOUNS	the Mississippi River	New York City	the South
COMMON NOUNS	a mighty river	a large city	a wind from the south

EXERCISE A   Add the missing capital letters in the following sentences. (Add 2 points for each correct answer.)

A. My friend betty underwood has traveled all over the united states.

1. Although she now lives in the east, she liked living in california best.

2. Her family has moved from chicago to new york, to st. louis, and to san francisco.

3. The underwoods have tried to learn about each section of the country in which they lived.

4. Because they like the water, they always try to find a house near a lake, river, or shoreline.

5. Now they live in a suburb north of boston called wayland and swim in lake cochichuate.

6. When the underwoods lived in san francisco, their house was only a block from san francisco bay.

7. Betty loved to cross the golden gate bridge and ride the cable cars on california street.

8. Her sister, alicia, attended classes at the university of california at berkeley.

9. She had a friend who was a buddhist and another who was a moslem.

10. The moslems follow the teachings of mohammed.

11. When the family moved to st. louis, they had trouble finding a home near the water.

12. The mississippi river is too muddy to swim in, and its current is very swift.

13. In chicago, the family lived in wilmette at 187 tenth avenue.

14. After betty finishes college, she wants to travel in europe and africa.

15. She wants to live in paris and study at the university of paris.

16. She would visit the louvre and study the paintings of monet and cassatt.

EXERCISE B Supply capital letters as you would if the following word groups were *within* sentences. (Add 10 points for each correctly marked item.)

1. in north carolina

2. near chicago

3. under mike's car

4. margaret mead

5. beyond lake superior

6. on the ferry to cape charles

7. the north wind

8. on riverside drive

9. the nearest lake

10. the atlantic ocean

More Proper Nouns

Capitalize the names of organizations, institutions, and government bodies.

EXAMPLES   Morton Junior High School   Girl Scouts of America
Meridian Building   Spanaway Lumber Company
the United States Senate   the Bureau of the Census

Do not capitalize words like *school, circus, restaurant, club,* or *building,* unless they are part of a proper name.

EXAMPLES   We passed a grade school, a church, and Roosevelt High School.
This building is not the Bowman Building.

Capitalize special events and calendar items.

EXAMPLES   This year Passover will begin on a Wednesday.
Labor Day is always on the first Monday in September.
Thanksgiving is the fourth Thursday in November.
Arnie wants to see the World Series.

Do *not* capitalize the names of the seasons.

EXAMPLE   My favorite time of the year is autumn.

Capitalize historical documents, events, and periods.

EXAMPLES   the Declaration of Independence
the Boston Tea Party

EXERCISE A In the blank at the left of column *A*, write the letter *A* or *B* to indicate which column contains the correctly capitalized phrase. (Add 5 points for each correct answer.)

COLUMN A	COLUMN B
.... 1. the Red cross	the Red Cross
.... 2. the Baker Medical Building	the Baker Medical building
.... 3. Freemont junior high school	Freemont Junior High School
.... 4. world war I	World War I
.... 5. a modern building	a modern Building
.... 6. the Roman Empire	the Roman empire

COLUMN A	COLUMN B
.... 7. The Rivera Supply company	the Rivera Supply Company
.... 8. Memorial day	Memorial Day
.... 9. Trinity Church	Trinity church
.... 10. Arcadia Motor Company	Arcadia Motor company
.... 11. our new School	our new school
.... 12. Wing's Bakery Shop	Wing's Bakery shop
.... 13. the supreme court	the Supreme Court
.... 14. United States congress	United States Congress
.... 15. Northwestern University	Northwestern university
.... 16. the fourth of July	the Fourth of July
.... 17. the Bureau of mines	the Bureau of Mines
.... 18. last summer	last Summer
.... 19. the U.S. National Tennis Tournament	the U.S. national tennis tournament
.... 20. April fool's day	April Fool's Day

EXERCISE B Add capital letters where necessary in the following sentences. (Add 2 points for each correct answer.)

1. I will start my job with the c. o. miller company next monday.

2. We are studying the art of the italian renaissance.

3. Classes at wade junior high school start on the thursday after labor day.

4. The National science fair takes place right after spring vacation.

5. I enjoyed the clyde beatty circus, which came to town last saturday.

6. Veterans' day was originally called armistice day, in commemoration of the end of world war I on november 11, 1918.

7. We visited the united states senate, the house of representatives, and the treasury building during our student tour of washington, D.C.

8. They attended martin luther king jr. high school in akron, ohio.

9. The moon lamp Company has its main office in the terminal building.

10. During the fall and winter there are several holidays, such as thanksgiving, christmas, and New year's day.

Proper Adjectives

Proper adjectives are words made from proper nouns and used as adjectives.

PROPER NOUNS	Italy	Shakespeare	England
PROPER ADJECTIVES	Italian	Shakespearean	English

Capitalize proper adjectives.

EXAMPLES
Elizabethan England   Christian theology
a Parisian scene   Greek art
Danish furniture   a Jewish holiday
Jeffersonian democracy   Victorian literature
French toast   the Muslim calendar

Note: A few proper adjectives have become so much a part of our language that they are no longer capitalized: *india rubber, china dishes.*

Notice that the nouns that are used with proper adjectives are not capitalized.

EXAMPLES   German shepherd   French poodle

Do not capitalize the names of school subjects, except languages and course names followed by a number.

EXAMPLES   I have finished my homework for French and English, but I still have an assignment to do for history.

The guidance counselor tells me I cannot take trigonometry until I have had Algebra II .

EXERCISE A   Supply capitals where needed in the following sentences. (Add 4 points for each correct answer.)

A. Some people think jazz is native *a*merican music.

1. Most jazz rhythms come from african music.

2. Great jazz can be heard in louisiana.

3. The original jazz bands were the bourbon street groups which marched in funerals in new orleans.

4. Two famous jazz performers were billie holiday and duke ellington.

5. West Indian music, such as the trinidadian calypso, is a mixture of african and spanish influences.

6. The jamaican steel bands produce a unique sound.

7. The ingenious jamaicans play fantastic music on instruments made from old oil drums and other nonmusical scrap.

8. To enjoy oneself in puerto rico, one needs to know a little spanish, which is the official language.

9. The puerto ricans have always been very proud of their spanish heritage.

10. Most tourists come back from puerto rico eager to learn the latin american dances.

EXERCISE B Supply capital letters wherever necessary in the following word groups as you would if they were used *within* sentences. Some items do not have to be changed. (Add 4 points for each correctly marked item.)

A. a chinese painting

1. georgian architecture
2. in science I
3. danish glassware
4. some canadian bacon
5. an english accent
6. moorish designs
7. a russian scientist
8. a typical new england village
9. china dishes
10. afro-american history
11. a social studies course
12. italian cooking
13. second-year german
14. algebra
15. home economics
16. plane geometry II
17. an irish brogue
18. a scottish fling
19. french poetry
20. south american music
21. ancient roman sculpture
22. a course in roman history
23. mathematics IV
24. mathematical reasoning
25. navajo culture

Titles

Everyone has a name, but some people also have a title which is used with their name to show position, respect, or relationship.

Capitalize a person's title when it comes before the name.

EXAMPLES   We spoke to Vice-President Malcolm in his office.
The fleet is under the command of Admiral Wendell Prescott.
The letter is addressed to the Rabbi Isaac Rubin.

A title is not usually capitalized when it follows the person's name or refers to the office in general.

EXAMPLES   the vice president of a bank   the captain of a ship
Mr. Gabel, the president of the company,

Some titles, particularly those of high government officials, are capitalized when used *instead of* the person's name or to show special respect for the office.

EXAMPLES   We saw the President on television last night.
She had an audience with the Pope.
Your Honor, here is the plaintiff.

Words that show family relationships are capitalized like other titles when they come before a person's name. When you use such words by themselves, in place of the person's name, you may capitalize them or not, as you prefer.

EXAMPLES   Uncle George   Aunt Lucy   Grandfather Martin

CORRECT   I expect Father will be home any minute.
ALSO CORRECT   I expect father will be home any minute.

Do *not* capitalize words of family relationship when they are used after a possessive of any kind.

EXAMPLES   my mother   your father   Mary Ann's grandfather   her uncle

Capitalize words referring to the Deity.

EXAMPLES   the Lord   our Father   Jehovah   the Supreme Being

However, when a word refers to a god of ancient mythology, it is not capitalized.

EXAMPLES   the Norse gods   the deities of ancient Greece

Capitalize the first word and all important words in titles of books, magazines, newspapers, poems, and stories.

Prepositions, articles, and conjunctions within titles are usually not capitalized.

EXAMPLES I have just finished reading *Shadows on the Rock* by Willa Cather.
My parents like the magazine *Scientific American*.
My favorite poem is "The Cremation of Sam McGee."
Have you read "Summer Water and Shirley," the short story by Durango Mendoza?

EXERCISE Supply all the missing capitals in the following sentences. Most sentences require more than one capital letter. (Add 4 points for each correct answer.)

1. In the Greek play *oedipus rex* the gods play a major role in people's lives.

2. Aunt Edna, have you seen our copy of the Sunday *news and observer?*

3. The book I am reading, *baseball is a funny game,* is very amusing.

4. At the board meeting, president Polanski proposed that our company sponsor a local soccer team.

5. The *saturday evening post* is a very popular magazine.

6. My sister has been elected president of the student council.

7. We are going to watch aunt Rona repair the calliope she bought from the Barnum and Bailey Circus.

8. One of Texas' most active representatives in the 1970's was congresswoman Barbara Jordan.

9. Most of the religions in the world are based on belief in god, the supreme being.

10. When Jamaica became independent, the United States was represented at the ceremonies by vice-president Johnson.

11. If you are interested in horses, I would certainly recommend *king of the wind* by Marguerite Henry.

12. Herman wrote a letter to senator Williams about one of the bills before congress.

Chapter Review

EXERCISE A   Supply capital letters as you would if the following word groups occurred *within* sentences. Some of the word groups are correct. Titles of poems and short stories are in quotation marks, and book and magazine titles are in italics. (Add 4 points for each correctly marked item.)

1. the louisiana purchase
2. *treasure island*
3. my father
4. "a boy with a dog"
5. lake michigan
6. "the lady or the tiger"
7. ambassador mabel smythe
8. catholics and protestants
9. south africa
10. *a wind from the north*
11. this year's strawberry festival
12. the synagogue on the corner
13. a grecian vase
14. english history
15. dawson creek
16. the east india company
17. wednesday, august fifteenth
18. our family doctor
19. history II
20. the ohio state historical society
21. the spanish-american war
22. congresswoman chisholm
23. Thanksgiving day
24. spring fever
25. the united states senate

EXERCISE B   Correct the capitalization of the paragraph below. Where a capital letter has been omitted, draw a line through the small letter and write the capital letter above it. Merely draw a line through any incorrect capital letter that you find. (Add 2 points for each correct answer.)

INFLUENCES FROM OTHER LANDS

1   Anyone who has studied American History knows that our country
2   was settled by people from many lands. Not all of us, however, realize
3   how much their customs still influence our daily life.
4   A glance at a map of the united States shows some of the main foreign
5   influences in the place names themselves. In the east we find many
6   Dutch names like hoboken, brooklyn, and harlem. In the West and
7   southwest we find spanish names like San francisco and Nevada. In
8   the Middle west and the south, french explorers and settlers left their

9   mark in names like La Crosse and Dubuque, Baton rouge and new
10 Orleans.

11   New Orleans, indeed, is a good example of the way another culture
12 has affected american life. Many of its Streets still bear such French
13 names as Toulouse street and Gravier Street. The architecture of the
14 French quarter recalls parts of paris. Its restaurants are famous for their
15 French Dishes.

16   The influences that have shaped our country turn up in some surpris-
17 ing places. Many of New england's Churches, for example, have the
18 classic lines of a greek Temple dedicated to the ancient Gods. In the
19 Southeast, a few mansions built before the American revolution recall
20 the architecture of elizabethan England. Some of california's churches,
21 founded by early catholic missionaries, would be equally at home in
22 Spain.

23   America's food, too, has been influenced by many cultures. Who has
24 not at some time enjoyed chinese fried rice, italian pasta, danish pastry,
25 or the german and scandinavian cheeses of wisconsin? The Smorgasbord
26 may seem as american as apple pie but the idea originated in sweden.
27 Pretzels and crullers were originally dutch delicacies. Shish kebab, which
28 is often served at Barbecues, is actually a turkish dish. Frankfurters and
29 hamburgers come to us from germany. They were named after the towns
30 where they originated, frankfort and hamburg. Bagels and knishes are
31 popular jewish dishes. No thanksgiving dinner would be complete
32 without Turkey, corn, and pumpkin pie. These dishes are truly american
33 for they came to us from the american Indians living here long before the
34 pilgrims reached our shore.

Cumulative Review

A Identify the parts of speech of the italicized words in the following sentences. Use the standard abbreviations. (Add 5 points for each correct answer.)

1   My *sister* is a *competent* person. She *carefully* drew up plans *for* a boat

2   which she is building in the *garage*. She saved the money and *bought* the

3   *finest* marine *plywood*. Because *she* is *following* the plans *exactly*, she *will*

4   have a *handsome craft*.

Identify the part of the sentence of each of the italicized words. Use the standard abbreviations: *subj., v., d.o.,* and *s.c.*

5   Our *cousins* Nina and Sue are helping her. My sister has given·to me the

6   *job* of sweeping up shavings. I am a good *sweeper,* she says. I *asked* her

7   what she planned to name the boat. *Nina* and Sue want to call it the

8   *Goof-off,* but I think my sister wants a more dignified *name*.

B Underline the subordinate clause in each sentence and in the blank write *adj.* for an adjective clause and *adv.* for an adverb clause. (Add 20 points for each correctly marked sentence.)

.... 1. Mesa Verde National Park is the area in which you find the homes of the ancient Cliff Dwellers.

.... 2. They built their homes in the inaccessible cliffs which exist in the buttes.

.... 3. Since there was no room to spare on the cliffs, they planted their crops on the canyon bottoms.

.... 4. When they saw a war party coming, they would retreat to the cliff dwelling and pull up all the ladders.

.... 5. Because they were peaceful, they became prosperous and built neat apartments between the sheer walls of stone.

C Punctuate the following sentences by adding capitals, commas, apostrophes, quotation marks, and end marks wherever needed. (Add 20 points for each correctly marked sentence.)

1. Band practice will be at 6:30 tomorrow evening said Marty

2. Can we make it later asked Sheila I usually have dinner at 6:30

3. Marty inquired can everyone make it if we change the time to 7:30

4. I may be a few minutes late said Carl but basically the times all right with me

5. Ill see you all tonight then said Marty

D Identify the following word groups as run-on sentences (*R*), fragments (*F*), or sentences (*S*). (Add 10 points for each correct answer.)

.... 1. Playing a phonograph record is really very easy, all you need is a turntable, a receiver, and speakers.

.... 2. What actually happens within the record-playing system is more complex.

.... 3. As the record turns, the stylus tracks the record's grooves.

.... 4. While the cartridge, to which the stylus is attached, translates these grooves into electricity measuring only thousandths of a volt.

.... 5. This electricity then feeds into the preamplifier circuit of the receiver, where it is increased enough to drive the amplifier.

.... 6. The preamplifier also acts as an equalizer, it can cut or boost the signals from high sounds or from low sounds, depending on the setting of your tone controls.

.... 7. The amplifier increases the strength of the electric signals even more, then it sends them to the speakers.

.... 8. The speaker cones help transform electrical energy back to mechanical energy.

.... 9. Which then reaches your ears as sound waves.

.... 10. Have you ever seen a very large speaker cone moving back and forth when a record is being played?

Building Vocabulary: Synonyms and Antonyms

<u>Synonyms</u> are words which have nearly the same meaning.
<u>Antonyms</u> are words which have nearly opposite meanings.

In the following example, the words in parentheses are all synonyms for each other—they have the same general meaning, "to become less."

SYNONYMS Toward evening, the violence of the storm (decreased, abated, dwindled).

Notice that although these three verbs are close in meaning and could all be used in this sentence, they do not have *exactly* the same meaning. *To decrease* means "to grow less little by little" and is the most general of the three words. *To abate* means "to grow gradually less" and is used of things that were excessive—too big, too violent—to begin with. (*Abate* is probably the most exact word to use to describe what happens to the storm in the example above.) *To dwindle* means "to melt away to nothing." We would say that the violence of the storm *dwindled* only if we meant that its violence decreased to the point of disappearing.

In the following sentence, the word *increase* is the opposite, an antonym, of *decrease, abate,* and *dwindle.*

ANTONYMS Toward evening, the violence of the storm *increased.*

This sentence means the opposite of the one above. The verb *to increase* has the general meaning "to become greater."

As you study the following definitions, try to think of at least one synonym and one antonym for each word.

brusque /brusk/, *adj.* Rough and short in manner and speech, though not necessarily rude.

casual /kázh ū əl/, *adj.* Relaxed and easy-going; of events, happening unpredictably, by chance.

confine /kən fín/, *v.* To keep within limits.

conjecture /kən jék chər/, *n.* A conclusion formed by guesswork or from too little evidence.

delude /di lúd/, *v.* To mislead and confuse people so that they cannot tell true from false.

ethical /éth i kəl/, *adj.* In accordance with *ethics,* rules of right conduct.

excessive /ik sés iv/, *adj.* More than enough; going beyond what is right or necessary.

hostility /hos tíl ə tē/, *n.* A strong and obvious feeling of dislike, especially for a person.

sever /sév ər/, *v.* To separate; to cut something apart from something else; to cut something in two.

successor /sək sés ər/, *n.* One who follows someone else in a job or an office.

EXERCISE One of the words defined in the list above is italicized in each sentence. In the first space at the left, under *S* for *synonym,* write the letter of the best synonym for the italicized word. In the second space, under *A* for *antonym,* write the letter of the best antonym. Check your answers in a dictionary. (Add 5 points for each correct answer.)

.... 1. Marsha's *brusque* manner often offends people.
a. angry   b. curt   c. gracious   d. mean

.... 2. Ford was Nixon's *successor* as President.
a. predecessor b. enemy   c. follower   d. friend

.... 3. As the dog grew older, we had to *confine* it in the yard.
a. restrict   b. release   c. capture   d. convey

.... 4. Your ideas about the Kingstons are based on *conjecture*.
a. certainty   b. contact   c. habit   d. surmise

.... 5. Cheating on a test is hardly *ethical*.
a. safe   b. sensible   c. moral   d. wicked

.... 6. *Excessive* speed is not the only cause of motor accidents.
a. average   b. insufficient c. extreme   d. stable

.... 7. Lack of respect can *sever* even the closest friends.
a. link   b. divide   c. destroy   d. harden

.... 8. People often feel *hostility* for those who are better off.
a. respect   b. antagonism c. anger   d. affection

.... 9. Geraldo is a *casual* acquaintance of mine, not a friend.
a. chance   b. young   c. recent   d. regular

.... 10. Do not *delude* yourself about your chances of winning.
a. persuade   b. praise   c. enlighten   d. deceive

REVIEW EXERCISE To the left of each italicized word, write the letter of
the best meaning. (Add 10 points for each correct answer.)

.... 1. the teachers *alternate*   a. to rest

.... 2. we must *resume* our work   b. to send back

.... 3. *remit* your payment   c. to change by turns

.... 4. *repose* in a hammock   d. theory or guess

.... 5. *inoculation* for typhoid   e. necessary

.... 6. *exasperate* one's parents   f. to take up, begin again

.... 7. an *indispensable* food   g. offensively bold

.... 8. a *wistful* expression   h. to make exceedingly angry

.... 9. *speculation* about life   i. substance that prevents disease

.... 10. *impertinent* remark   j. sad and longing

Spelling: Doubling Final Consonants in Words of More Than One Syllable

The rule you learned in Lesson 65 about doubling the final consonant is an excellent spelling guide, but unfortunately it applies only to words of one syllable. Can you state that rule about one-syllable words?

Now look at what happens to words of *more* than one syllable ending in a single consonant preceded by a single vowel when suffixes that begin with vowels are added. Try to figure out why the final consonant is *not* doubled in the words in column *1* and why it *is* doubled for those in column *2*. (Notice which syllable is accented in each word in columns *1* and *2*.)

1		*2*	
ópen + ing = ópening		refér + ing = reférring	
lísten + er = lístener		begín + er = begínner	
devélop + ed = devéloped		decontról + ed = decontrólled	

On which syllable are all the words in column *2* accented? Which is accented in column *1*? All the words in column *2* have the strong accent on the *last* syllable. Pronounce *re fér, be gín,* and *de con tról.* Where is the strong accent in the words in column *1*? Say *ó pen, lís ten,* and *de vél op.* It is *not* on the last syllable. In *ópen* and *lísten* it is on the first syllable; in *devélop,* it is on the middle or second syllable.

Here is a rule that will generally help you decide whether or not to double the final consonant in such words.

In adding a suffix beginning with a vowel to words of more than one syllable ending in a single consonant preceded by a single vowel, double the final consonant if the word is accented on the *last* syllable.

(Do *not* double the final consonant in such words if the accent is not on the last syllable.)

Once in a while the accent mark in a word will shift when a suffix is added. In the first example in column *2, refer* became *referring* when the suffix *–ing* was added. In both *refér* and *reférring* the accent is on the *–fer.* But see what happens to the accent of *refer* when the suffix *–ence* is added. Pronounce the word *reference.* On which syllable is the strong accent? The first.

As you see, the rule was followed by doubling the final consonant in *refer* (to make *referring*) because the accent *remained* on the *–fer* syllable. It was *not* doubled in *reference,* because when *refer* became *reference* the accent shifted to the first syllable of the new word—*réference.* The rule applied in both cases.

147

EXERCISE A Add the indicated suffixes to the following words. Write the new words in the blanks. Remember the importance of accented syllables in deciding whether or not to double the final consonant. (Add 5 points for each correctly spelled word.)

1. omit + ed = ...
2. excel + ing = ...
3. benefit + ed = ...
4. glisten + ing = ...
5. prefer + ence = ...
6. repel + ed = ...
7. compel + ing = ...
8. occur + ing = ...
9. fidget + ed = ...
10. alter + ing = ...

11. control + able = ...
12. differ + ence = ...
13. commit + ed = ...
14. regret + ing = ...
15. forget + able = ...
16. utter + ance = ...
17. wonder + ing = ...
18. encounter + ed = ...
19. prefer + ing = ...
20. defer + ence = ...

EXERCISE B Add *–ence* to each of the following words. Write the new words in the blanks. (Add 25 points for each correctly spelled word.)

1. infer + ence = ...
2. transfer + ence = ...

3. occur + ence = ...
4. concur + ence = ...

REVIEW EXERCISE Be prepared to write the following words from dictation. (Add 10 points for each correctly spelled word.)

1. cubed
2. webbing
3. sadden
4. slimmest
5. griper

6. ruder
7. caning
8. scrubbing
9. reddish
10. diced

CHAPTER EIGHT

Using Pronouns Correctly

There are a good many English words which can be used as pronouns, but the ones called personal pronouns cause more than their share of trouble. The reason for this is that most of the personal pronouns have two different forms—a *subject form* and an *object form.* Notice that only *you* and *it* are the same in both the subject and the object form.

SUBJECT PRONOUNS	OBJECT PRONOUNS
I—we	me—us
you	you
he, she, it—they	him, her, it—them

Before you can be sure which form is correct, you must know how the pronoun is used in the sentence. Fortunately, there are a few simple rules for choosing the correct pronouns and avoiding pronoun blunders. By the time you complete this chapter, you should know them all.

LESSON 74

Pronouns as Subjects

Only the subject forms of the personal pronouns may be used as the subjects of sentences and subordinate clauses: I—we, you, he, she, it—they.

EXAMPLES   We collect aluminum cans for recycling.   (sentence)

After the concert she could not find her friends.   (sentence)

When they travel abroad, their neighbors watch the house. (subordinate clause)

People who have no trouble with pronouns in sentences like those above may be thoroughly confused by compound subjects. The following examples are incorrect because they make object pronouns (*them, us*) the subjects. An object pronoun should never be used as the subject of a verb in standard English.

NONSTANDARD   *Them or the teacher* must surely remember.
NONSTANDARD   Next week *Bert and us* are going away.

If you have trouble choosing the correct pronoun in compound subjects, use this method to help you decide: (1) Find the subject of the sentence. (2) In your mind, drop out all of the subject except the pronoun. It will then be obvious that you need the subject form as the subject of the verb.

STANDARD   They ~~or the teacher~~ <u>must</u> surely <u>remember</u>.

STANDARD   Next week, ~~Bert and~~ <u>we</u> <u>are going</u> away.

Remember that personal pronouns, like all other pronouns, take the place of one or more nouns, with their modifiers. We use *we, they,* and sometimes *you* when we are talking about more than one person or thing, and *I, he, she, it,* and sometimes *you* when we are talking about only one person or thing.

EXAMPLES   the boys = they   Shirley and I = we
                you and Mike = you   the red house on the corner = it

EXERCISE   In the space to the right of each sentence, write one personal pronoun that can replace the word or words in italics. (Add 10 points for each correct answer.)

A. *Hilda* brought her sister a new record.   A. ...*She*...

1. *Tania Atwater* is a leading scientist studying earth-   1. ....
quakes.

2. *My next-door neighbors and I* went camping.   2. ....

3. *Our old car* got better mileage than the new one.   3. ....

4. Do *people in glass houses* worry about stones?   4. ....

5. *Ruth and I* are both in the school orchestra.   5. ....

Underline the correct one of the two pronouns in the parentheses. Remember that only the subject form is used as the subject of a sentence or of a subordinate clause.

6. Danny and (I, me) took sailing lessons last summer.

7. What time did you and (he, him) get home yesterday?

8. (They, Them) are the best students in the whole school.

9. If (she, her) or Dad asks you, explain what happened.

10. Both Bernice and (she, her) are taking French.

Pronouns as Subject Complements

A *subject complement* is a word that comes after the verb and refers to the subject. When a subject complement is a noun or pronoun, it means the same person or thing as the subject.

The subject forms of the personal pronouns should be used as subject complements.

EXAMPLES   It is she.

The man wearing the red carnation will be he.

The ones in the back row were we.

The girls who planned the exhibit must have been they.

A subject and a subject complement are connected by a *linking verb.* When the subject complement is a pronoun, the linking verb is always a form of the verb *to be* (*am, is, are—was, were—been*). Helping verbs (like *will* and *must have* in the examples above) may be used with the linking verb.

Since the subject and the subject complement refer to the same thing, we can usually turn them around without changing the meaning of the sentence. If you are not sure which pronoun to use, try the complement out as the subject to make sure.

EXAMPLE   The girl on the bicycle must have been (she, her).

She must have been the girl on the bicycle. (Only *she,* the subject form of the pronoun, fits the subject slot in this sentence. Therefore, *she* is the correct form to use as the subject complement.)

We use the subject form of the pronoun when the subject complement is *compound* (connected by *and* or *or* with a noun or another pronoun). In such cases, you can avoid a pronoun blunder by mentally dropping out the other part of the subject complement.

NONSTANDARD   The winners were the Gilley twins and *them.*
STANDARD   The winners were the Gilley twins and they.

NONSTANDARD   It will probably be you and *him* in the finals.
STANDARD   It will probably be you and he in the finals.

(The common expressions *It's me, It's her, It's him, It's us,* and *It's them,* which are used only in spoken English, are acceptable even though they do not follow the rule that subject complements are in the subjective case. While both *It's I* and *It's me,* for example, are standard, *It's me* is much more commonly used in spoken English.)

EXERCISE A Underline the correct one of the two pronouns in the parentheses. Remember that only the subject form is used as a subject complement.
(Add 10 points for each correct answer.)

1. The best spellers in the class are you and (she, her).

2. The ones who played those Halloween pranks must have been (they, them).

3. The person you are looking for could be (she, her).

4. The new editor of the yearbook will be (he, him).

5. The players in the first match will be Chris Evert Lloyd and (she, her).

6. That must be (she, her) and the Williamsons in the front row.

7. If it had been Omar and (I, me), we would have told you.

8. The two you are talking about might possibly have been Andrea and (she,
   her), but they certainly could not have been (we, us).

9. If it was not (he, him) at the top of the stairs, I can't guess who it was.

EXERCISE B If the italicized pronoun in each sentence is correct, write the
letter C in the blank to the right of each sentence. If the pronoun is *not* correct,
cross it out and write the correct form in the blank. (Add 10 points for each
correctly marked sentence.)

A. The captain of the ship is *him* over there.   A. ...*he*.....

1. The unknown caller may be *she*.   1. ....

2. In the book, the murderer was *her*.   2. ....

3. It was Anne and *us* who used the Sanchez' car.   3. ....

4. No, it was *they* who had that noisy party.   4. ....

5. The person in charge of mowing the lawn is *her*.   5. ....

6. The last one we thought of was *him*.   6. ....

7. If it is Murray and *they*, ask them to come in.   7. ....

8. The next time monitors are chosen, they might be *us*. 8. ....

9. Our only winner was *him*.   9. ....

10. If you were *her*, what would you do?   10. ....

152

Pronouns as Direct Objects

Only the object forms of the personal pronouns may be used as the objects of verbs: me—us, him, her, them.

The object of a verb, or *direct object,* receives the action of the verb and usually comes after it.

EXAMPLES   Mrs. Roberts drove us to the stadium.

I asked him to solve the puzzle.

Notice that the direct object always follows an action verb. Do not confuse the direct object with a subject complement, which follows the linking verb *to be* and refers to the same person or thing as the subject. A direct object requires the object form of a pronoun. A subject complement takes the subject form.

DIRECT OBJECT   Gerard met her at school yesterday.

SUBJECT COMPLEMENT It was she whom Gerard met at school yesterday.

When you use a noun and a pronoun (or two pronouns) together as objects of the same verb, try them out separately to make sure which form of the pronoun to use.

NONSTANDARD   They met my *father and I* at the station. (They met *I* at the station.)

STANDARD   They met my father and me at the station. (They met *me* at the station.)

NONSTANDARD   Why didn't we see *you or he* at the meeting? (Why didn't we see *he?*)

STANDARD   Why didn't we see you or him at the meeting? (Why didn't we see *him?*)

EXERCISE A Underline the correct one of the two pronouns in the parentheses. Remember that only the object form is used as a direct object. (Add 10 points for each correct answer.)

1. Mrs. Rosen took Becky, two other girls, and (I, me) to the circus.

2. He and I saw you and (they, them) before anyone else.

3. If it worries you or (she, her), you shouldn't do it.

4. Do your parents want you and (we, us) home early tonight?

5. Please don't leave his dog and (he, him) out in the rain.

6. You should have let Jill or (she, her) make the announcement.

7. We should pick the girls and (he, him) up in our car.

8. It must have taken (he, him) or (she, her) an hour to finish.

9. The Drakes will meet you and (I, me), I suppose.

EXERCISE B Some of the pronouns in this story are printed in italics. Draw a line through any italicized pronoun that is incorrect and write the correct form above it. Some of the pronouns are used as subjects, some as subject complements, and some as direct objects. If you are in doubt about any pronoun, take time to decide whether it is used as a subject, a subject complement, or a direct object. Some of the italicized pronouns are correct. (Add 5 points for each correct answer.)

1   Howard, Bruce, and *me* camped out at Lost Lake over the weekend.

2   On Friday afternoon, my parents drove *us* and our camping equipment

3   to the lake in the station wagon. Howard's parents had arranged to pick

4   Howard and *we* up again Sunday night. It was *they* who insisted on

5   our taking plenty of food. *He* and *she* knew more about fishing in Lost

6   Lake than *us* boys did. Howard was expecting to catch fish for supper,

7   and even Bruce and *me* had visions of trout frying in the pan.

8   Howard was in a hurry to make camp before dark. *Him* and *me* put

9   up the tent while Bruce gathered wood. Then Howard said, "Joe, you

10   and *him* get the fire ready for supper. I'll take care of the fishing. Would

11   you help Bruce and *me* while we put the canoe into the water?"

12   Bruce and *me* soon had the frying pan sizzling. An hour passed and

13   still *us* two were hungrily waiting for Howard to get back with his catch.

14   *Him* and *I* wondered what had happened to the great fisher. At last

15   Bruce and *I* saw a dark shape approaching. We were sure it was *him*

16   in the canoe. I shouted, "Hurry up! Are you trying to starve Bruce and

17   *me?*" Howard did not answer. In silence Bruce and *him* opened some

18   cans of tuna.

Pronouns After Prepositions

The noun or pronoun that comes after a preposition is called the *object* of the preposition.

Only the object forms of the personal pronouns may be used as the objects of prepositions: me—us, him, her, them.

EXAMPLES to me   for us   about him
          near her   concerning them

As usual, pronoun blunders are most likely to occur when the pronoun is used with a noun or another pronoun. To be sure of getting the pronoun correct, try it out by itself with the preposition.

NONSTANDARD Victoria drew a picture *of her sister and he.* (*of he*)
STANDARD   Victoria drew a picture of her sister and him. (*of him*)
NONSTANDARD Mrs. Perez gave the job *to she and I.* (*to she, to I*)
STANDARD   Mrs. Perez gave the job to her and me. (*to her, to me*)

EXERCISE A Underline the correct one of the two pronouns in the parentheses. Remember that only the object form is used as the object of a preposition. (Add 5 points for each correct answer.)

1. Can you come to the game with David and (I, me)?

2. I spoke to Lisa and (she, her) at our party.

3. Edith will go downtown with both Jean and (she, her).

4. These old books are for my cousin and (I, me).

5. Dan's mother received postcards from (he, him) and Bernardo.

6. Gordon is traveling in Mexico with Pete and (they, them).

7. Natalie brought these magazines for Diane and (I, me).

8. The letter was addressed to (he, him) and (she, her).

9. All of (they, them) are in the play with Don and (I, me).

10. I spoke to Inez and (he, him) about practicing after school.

11. The magazine was of interest to Sylvia and (I, me).

12. Because of Stacey and (he, him) the fire was reported in time.

13. Bess, will you wait for Mildred and (I, me) after school?

14. The committee will have a conference with Ms. Epstein and (I, me).

15. Yesterday I sat between (she, her) and Elaine at the game.

16. You will have to choose between (he, him) and (I, me).

17. I sat behind you and (he, him).

EXERCISE B Some of the following sentences contain pronoun errors. If the sentence is correct, write a *C* in the blank at the right. If there is an error, cross out the incorrect pronoun and write the correct pronoun form in the blank. (Add 10 points for each correctly marked sentence.)

1. The argument between Geraldo and *I* was not
serious.   1. . . . .

2. The stories written by Jaime and *her* were the best.   2. . . . .

3. Fatigue affected the playing of both his partner
and *he*.   3. . . . .

4. To my parents and *us* the movie was disappointing.   4. . . . .

5. We received letters from the Rileys and *they*.   5. . . . .

6. Someone has been looking for Greta and *she*.   6. . . . .

7. Who was sitting beside you and *he?*   7. . . . .

8. Are you going to the game with Arno and *I?*   8. . . . .

9. Everyone was on time except you and *them.*   9. . . . .

10. I have faith in Sarah and *her.*   10. . . . .

Three Pronoun Blunders

Probably the most common pronoun blunders in standard English are those that occur when a pronoun is joined by *and* or *or* to a noun or another pronoun. There are three other pronoun problems for which you should watch out.

1. Us Boys—Us Girls Can you see what is the matter with this sentence?

NONSTANDARD *Us boys* have a baseball game tonight.

In the example, *boys* is an appositive explaining *us.* It can be left out and the sentence will still be complete without it. Drop *boys* and you can see at once that *us* is incorrect. *Us* is an object pronoun and cannot be the subject of the sentence.

NONSTANDARD *Us* boys have a baseball game tonight.
STANDARD We ~~boys~~ have a baseball game tonight.

An expression like "us boys" is correct only when the object pronoun *us* is used as the object of a verb or preposition.

OBJECT OF VERB They have invited us girls over for a swim.
OBJECT OF A PREPOSITION Overeating is a weakness of many of us mortals.

2. Duplicate Subject Do not let an unnecessary pronoun slip in after the subject of a sentence. The duplicate subject adds nothing to the meaning and should be omitted.

NONSTANDARD Mildred, *she* will come to our party.
STANDARD Mildred will come to our party.

NONSTANDARD Bill and I, *we* have only just heard about it.
STANDARD Bill and I have only just heard about it.

3. The Courteous I It is not considered courteous to mention oneself first. In a compound subject or object, *I* or *me* should come at the end.

NONSTANDARD *I and Andy* will come early.
STANDARD Andy and I will come early.

NONSTANDARD Miss Dietz made *me and Sheila* the class monitors.
STANDARD Miss Dietz made Sheila and me the class monitors.

EXERCISE A Draw a line through any unnecessary pronoun that duplicates the subject. If the wrong form of a pronoun is used, draw a line through it and write the correct form after the number of the sentence in the space to the right. Change any violations of the "courteous I." Write *C* after the number of any sentence that is correct as it stands. (Add 10 points for each correctly marked sentence.)

1. Several of we eighth-graders work on the school newspaper.   1. . . . .

2. The ninth-graders they work on the newspaper too.   2. . . . .

3. I and Karen Michaelson are reporters.   3. . . . .

4. She and I also worked on the paper last year.   4. . . . .

5. Mr. Posnick he is our supervisor.   5. . . . .

6. He suggests stories for we reporters to cover.   6. . . . .

7. Karen she thinks we need more reporters.   7. . . . .

8. The seventh-graders they would like to work on the paper, too.   8. . . . .

9. Most of us reporters consider this a good idea.   9. . . . .

10. Special seventh-grade events they can be covered by seventh-graders.   10. . . . .

EXERCISE B Underline the correct one of the two pronouns in the parentheses. (Add 10 points for each correct answer.)

AMERICANS ABROAD

1   (We, Us) Americans are sometimes misunderstood by people in other

2   countries. For many years, the only Americans Europeans saw were

3   tourists with more money than (they, them) had. Hollywood movies also

4   showed (we, us) Americans in a distorted light. The Europeans came

5   to think of all of (we, us) Americans as having too much money and

6   too little courtesy. Today, however, it is often (we, us) students who

7   travel in Europe. (We, Us) young people travel by bike and stay in youth

8   hostels. Many of (we, us) students live with families and show that we

9   can work at least as hard as (they, them) do. They, in turn, have learned

10   from (we, us) visitors about our customs. (We, Us) students who have

11   visited Europe have done much to give the Europeans an accurate

12   picture of the real America.

158

Chapter Review

EXERCISE A Each of the following sentences contains an italicized pronoun. In the blank to the left of each sentence, write one of these abbreviations to show how the pronoun is used in the sentence: *subj.* for *subject; d.o.* for *direct object; o.p.* for *object of preposition;* and *s.c.* for *subject complement.* (Add 10 points for each correct answer.)

.... 1. Many of *us* consider Robert Frost one of America's finest modern poets.

.... 2. It is *he* whom most people think of first when American poetry is mentioned.

.... 3. *He* has been popular for three generations.

.... 4. Most people like *him* for the surface clarity of his poems.

.... 5. With a second or third reading, however, *we* discover depths of meaning in his poems.

.... 6. Actually, Frost is often more profound than some other poets who seem more difficult than *he* does.

.... 7. At the Presidential inauguration in 1960, Frost received the official recognition which *he* had long deserved.

.... 8. Bareheaded in the chilling wind, he recited his poem "The Gift Outright" to all of *us* across the nation.

.... 9. In the same dry, weary voice, *he* read his poems to thousands of young people and adults.

.... 10. People all over the world will remember *him* for his poems and his way of talking about life.

EXERCISE B Circle the correct pronoun from the two in parentheses. If you are in doubt about which form of the pronoun is correct, stop and work out whether it is used as a subject, a subject complement, a direct object, or an object of a preposition. (Add 10 points for each correct answer.)

1. David, Inez and (I, me) went to the amusement park on Memorial Day.

2. Inez asked Dave and (I, me) whether we would go on the roller coaster.

3. Inez and (he, him) had never ridden a roller coaster before.

4. When we went down the first dip, David grabbed (we, us) and yelled.

5. I suggested the Bumpem Cars to (they, them).

159

6. Dave and I rode in a separate car from Inez and kept bumping into (she, her).

7. Inez asked (we, us) if we would buy tickets for the Ferris wheel.

8. Dave and I talked (she, her) into trying the "haunted house."

9. When the ghost jumped out, (we, us) all screamed.

10. Fireworks were set off at dusk, and we decided that (they, them) were the best part of the day.

EXERCISE C Draw a line through any incorrect personal pronoun form in the following sentences and write the correct form above it. If you find a pronoun that makes a duplicate subject, merely cross it out. (Add 10 points for each correctly marked sentence.)

1. Are these pencils for them or I?

2. Us and the ninth-graders have been especially busy this week.

3. It was they who complimented Priscilla and me on our work.

4. Bernice, she is staying for a conference with Mr. Crowley and I.

5. Could it have been us that she and him were talking about?

6. Ike and me have been making posters for the carnival next week.

7. The Murphy twins, they have invited Carole and he on a picnic.

8. Would you please take them back where they came from?

9. That must be him and her now!

10. The flowers are from Kevin and we, not from her and Susanne.

Cumulative Review

A Complete the following statements. (Add 10 points for each correct answer.)

1. A word used in place of a noun is a(n) . . . .

2. Adjectives modify . . . . and . . . .

3. A word that connects words or groups of words is a(n) . . . .

4. A word like *have, was,* or *might* that helps the main verb express its meaning is called a(n) . . . . verb.

5. A(n) . . . . is a group of words which begins with a preposition and ends with a noun or a pronoun.

6. A word in the predicate which means the same as or describes the subject is called a(n) . . . .

7. A noun or pronoun which receives the action of the verb is called a(n) . . . .

8. A sentence which has two or more independent clauses connected by *and, but,* or *or* is called a(n) . . . . sentence.

9. A clause which modifies a noun or a pronoun is a(n) . . . . clause.

B Underline the clauses in these sentences, and in the blank write *adj.* if the clause is an adjective clause or *adv.* if it is an adverb clause. (Add 10 points for each correctly marked sentence.)

. . . . 1. I am reading a book which I find hard to put down.

. . . . 2. It is the story of a journey that was made across the Pacific on a primitive raft.

. . . . 3. Because he wanted evidence for the South American origin of the Polynesians, Thor Heyerdahl attempted the difficult trip.

. . . . 4. Thor Heyerdahl and five companions set out on a small raft which they had made themselves.

. . . . 5. Even though I know the happy ending of his adventure, I still find the story of it tremendously exciting.

.... 6. After they had traveled for 101 days, they crash-landed on a coral reef.

.... 7. The sailors, who were all experienced at sea, learned to catch sharks with their bare hands.

.... 8. The raft *Kon-Tiki* was named after a god who is found in both Peruvian and Polynesian mythology.

.... 9. I read recently about a Japanese teen-ager who sailed to the Pacific Coast from Japan in a tiny boat.

.... 10. He attempted the crossing because he wanted to study in the United States.

C Identify the following groups of words as sentences (*S*), fragments (*F*), or run-on sentences (*R*). (Add 20 points for each correct answer.)

.... 1. The authorities inspected his little boat and meager equipment, they decided he must have been a superb navigator.

.... 2. Because he did not have a passport, visa, or other necessary papers.

.... 3. I think he showed great courage and determination and should be allowed to stay.

.... 4. True stories like these prove that the age of adventure is not over I should like to go on such a voyage some day.

.... 5. Which might carry me to the South Seas or perhaps to the Greek islands of the Mediterranean.

D Add the necessary punctuation and capital letters in these sentences. (Add 20 points for each correctly marked sentence.)

1. I can't be one of next years class officers because Im moving this summer.

2. Northeastern University is in boston and northwestern university is in evanston Illinois.

3. "Jack why wont you come with us I asked. we're only driving down to the lake.

4. "I've been invited to a meeting at grace episcopal church wayne said.

5. One of the new students has joined our dance group our french club and the girls soccer team.

Building Vocabulary: One-Word Definition

"Grab the *bow!*" shouts the sailor coming in to the dock, but if the person standing there looks blank and does nothing, the sailor might explain: "The *front* of the boat, you landlubber!"

Often, in conversation and in writing, we have to explain a word's meaning in order to be understood. We do so by using other, familiar words in place of the unfamiliar word, as in the example above. Such an explanation is called a *definition.*

A one-word definition is, of course, a *synonym* for the word defined. Not all synonyms, however, make good definitions. To be useful, a definition must pass two tests.

A good definition uses words that are more familiar than the word being defined.

A good definition can substitute for the word being defined.

Suppose, for example, that we needed a good one-word definition for *esteem* as it is used in the following sentence.

EXAMPLE   Mr. Hogland esteems Amy Lowell above all other poets.

Both *to praise* and *to appreciate* have the general meaning of "to approve," as does the verb *to esteem. To praise* and *to appreciate* are, therefore, synonyms for the verb *to esteem. Praise,* however, suggests showing one's approval in some way, while *appreciate* has to do with an inner feeling of approval. Since *esteem* is concerned only with how one feels about something (not what one does as a result), *appreciate,* not *praise,* would be the proper one-word definition.

EXAMPLE   Mr. Hogland appreciates Amy Lowell above all other poets.

The purpose of a definition is to make ourselves clear to others. Notice, however, that in doing this we often gain a better—clearer, more exact —understanding of word meanings ourselves. In trying to define *esteem,* we gained a better understanding both of it and of two closely related words, *appreciate* and *praise.*

Study the following definitions in preparation for the exercise that follows.

comply /kəm plí/, *v.* To give in and do what is wanted (usually with *with*).

conflagration /kón flə grā shən/, *n.* A large and destructive fire.

decompose /dḗ kəm póz/, *v.* To decay; to break down into original parts.

devout /di voút/, *adj.* Active and deeply convinced in matters of religion.

exacting /ig zák ting/, *adj.* Making many difficult demands.

external /ik stúr nəl/, *adj.* Related to the surface or exterior of something.

frenzy /frén zē/, *n.* Wild and uncontrolled emotional excitement of brief duration.

ingenious /in jén yəs/, *adj.* Showing unusual skill or mental ability.

ovation /ō vā´ shən/, *n.* An enthusiastic tribute by a group of people.

verify /vér ə fī/, *v.* To show that something is true by providing evidence or scientific proof; to check the accuracy of something.

EXERCISE Each italicized word is a one-word definition, or close synonym, for one of the words defined above. In the space at the right, write the word from this lesson that can replace the italicized word. Consult a dictionary if you are not sure of the meaning of the word in italics. (Add 10 points for each correct answer.)

1. The *fire* that destroyed the dock area of the city was probably started by lightning.

1. . . . .

2. We found the work extremely *demanding,* and by the end of the day, we were worn out.

2. . . . .

3. Willis must *agree* with the other tenants' request not to practice the violin after ten o'clock at night.

3. . . . .

4. In his first sermon, the new minister urged his congregation to be more *religious.*

4. . . . .

5. The *applause* that greeted the pianist's performance continued for fifteen minutes.

5. . . . .

6. If you want to convince an audience, it may be a mistake to use overly *clever* arguments.

6. . . . .

7. The defense lawyer argued that the accused had committed the crime in a moment of *madness.*

7. . . . .

8. Couldn't you see that the label said the medicine was for *outside* use only?

8. . . . .

9. The fallen tree, which had begun to *disintegrate,* was not much good as firewood.

9. . . . .

10. A good newspaper will not usually print a story which it cannot *confirm.*

10. . . . .

REVIEW EXERCISE To the left of each italicized word, write the letter of the best meaning. (Add 20 points for each correct answer.)

. . . . 1. an *alluring* appearance

. . . . 2. an *amphibious* creature

. . . . 3. *concur* in a decision

. . . . 4. *confine* to his room

. . . . 5. a *fretful* child

a. living on land and in water

b. worried and peevish

c. to keep within limits

d. mysteriously attractive

e. to agree

164

Spelling: Articulating Sounds

Many spelling errors are the result of careless and unclear speech. If you improve your *articulation,* you can probably eliminate quite a few spelling mistakes. Articulation refers to the distinctness or clarity of the sounds you make. Good articulation will make your spoken words sound better, as well as improve your spelling.

Say each group of words below, articulating as distinctly as you can. Pay special attention to the letters in red type.

1	*2*	*3*	*4*
told	kept	library	probably
find	fists	February	finally
width	interest	government	literature
grandmother	quantity	surprise	regular
handle			recognize
candidate			agreeable
hundred			poetry

5	*6*
which	fifth
whether	length
whale	strength

EXERCISE A   Form small groups of six students each. Each student will in turn dictate words from one of the six lists above to the rest of the pupils in the group. Articulate each word *you* dictate as clearly as you can, so that the other students in your group can write the words correctly.

EXERCISE B   Here are more words frequently misspelled because of sloppy articulation. Say each word clearly and correctly, particularly the letters in red type. Then be prepared to write the words as your teacher dictates them.

whine	mind
while	handmade
where	western
whisper	sixth
slept	jewelry
sifts	generally
lists	cruelly
congratulate	temperature

EXERCISE C On the board, have someone make a class list of twenty words suggested by class members (other than those taught in this lesson) that the class thinks are frequently misspelled because of careless articulation. Have someone copy the words and give them to the teacher. Then erase the words from the board. Now write the words in the blanks below as your teacher dictates them. (Add 5 points for each correctly spelled word.)

1. ....   11. ....
2. ....   12. ....
3. ....   13. ....
4. ....   14. ....
5. ....   15. ....
6. ....   16. ....
7. ....   17. ....
8. ....   18. ....
9. ....   19. ....
10. ....   20. ....

EXERCISE D Now prepare to write from dictation fifty of the words you have studied in this lesson. (Add 2 points for each correctly spelled word.)

REVIEW EXERCISE Be prepared to write the following words from dictation. (Add 10 points for each correctly spelled word.)

1. committed
2. regretting
3. occurrence
4. controllable
5. deference
6. forgettable
7. repelled
8. inference
9. beginner
10. benefited

CHAPTER NINE

Making Subjects and Verbs Agree

Usually, it makes a good deal of difference whether you are talking about one thing—one car, one ice cream cone, one ostrich—or about many. Most nouns and pronouns have different forms to show whether they mean *one* or *more than one.* So that there can be no doubt about it, verbs also usually have different forms for *one* or *more than one,* and you should be careful to use the right form of a verb with the right subject when using standard English. Most of the time, we match verb and subject automatically, but there are a few situations in which many people make mistakes. The best cure for such language blunders is the knowledge of the principles of *subject-verb agreement* which this chapter will give you.

LESSON 83

Singular and Plural

When a word refers to one person, place, thing, or idea, it is singular in number. When it refers to more than one, it is plural in number.

SINGULAR WORDS	girl	man	city	box	deer	democracy
PLURAL WORDS	girls	men	cities	boxes	deer	democracies

Most nouns change from singular to plural by adding *–s* or *–es.* Personal pronouns and nouns like *man, woman,* and *mouse* change in other ways. A small number of nouns are the same in both their singular and plural forms: *sheep, moose, deer.*

Notice that among the personal pronouns only *you* has the same form in both the singular and plural:

SINGULAR PRONOUNS	I	you	he, she, it
PLURAL PRONOUNS	we	you	they

EXERCISE A Indicate in the blank to the left of each word whether it is singular or plural. Write *S* for *singular, P* for *plural.* (Add 4 points for each correct answer.)

1. .... oxen

2. .... it

3. .... mountains

4. .... topcoat

5. .... women

6. .... breakfast

167

7. .... beaches
8. .... intelligence
9. .... we
10. .... babies
11. .... they
12. .... she
13. .... cupfuls
14. .... lamps
15. .... children
16. .... mice

17. .... chair
18. I
19. .... mother-in-law
20. .... assignment
21. .... carriages
22. .... nation
23. .... families
24. .... baseballs
25. .... tickets

EXERCISE B Change the words below from singular to plural or from plural to singular. If a word is singular, write the plural form in the blank. If it is plural, write the singular form. If a word is the same in both singular and plural, write it in the blank without change. (Add 4 points for each correct answer.)

1. cheese ....
2. sheep ....
3. goat ....
4. apples ....
5. team ....
6. ax ....
7. sauces.....................
8. airport ....
9. galaxies ....
10. mice ....
11. moose ....
12. gallery ....
13. barometers ....

14. we.....................
15. noises ....
16. adenoid ....
17. baseball ....
18. mountain lion ....
19. gentlemen ....
20. automobiles ....
21. skeletons ....
22. text ....
23. trout.....................
24. yacht ....
25. fishing rod.................

A Verb Agrees in Number with Its Subject

A verb *agrees* with its subject when both are in the same number.

A singular subject takes a singular verb. A plural subject takes a plural verb.

SINGULAR	PLURAL
The catcher needs practice.	The catchers need practice.
The skater has fallen down.	The skaters have fallen down.
His plant does not need water.	His plants do not need water.

Problems in subject-verb agreement arise chiefly when the subject is in the third person, which consists of all subjects except the pronouns *I, we,* and *you.* To make a verb agree with a third-person *singular* subject (*he, she, it,* or a singular noun), simply add the *s* verb ending to the verb. All other subjects take the verb form that does not end in *s.*

The one exception to this rule is that troublesome verb *to be.*

SINGULAR	PLURAL
I am, I was	we are, we were
you are, you were	you are, you were
he (she, it) is, he (she, it) was	they are, they were

EXERCISE A   Underline the subject of each sentence and the verb in the parentheses that agrees with the subject. (Add 10 points for each correctly marked sentence.)

A. Jordan's painting (was, were) extremely well done.

1. My sisters never (enjoys, enjoy) arguing any more.

2. Your friends (has, have) gone home by now.

3. The club members (is, are) planning an overnight hike.

4. You (turns, turn) left at the first stop light.

5. The mail carrier (delivers, deliver) the mail about noon.

6. The breeze (seems, seem) cooler this evening.

7. Some people really (does, do) live in glass houses.

8. A baby robin (eats, eat) its weight in worms every day.

9. We (was, were) driving to Trout Lake last week.

10. They (calls, call) two pheasants a "brace."

Don't and Doesn't   A contraction is a word formed by combining or shortening two or more words. The apostrophe shows where letters have been left out. *Doesn't* is short for *does not,* the form of the verb used only with *he, she, it,* and other third person singular subjects. *Don't* is short for *do not.* To make sure that you have the correct one of this troublesome pair, think of the contraction as if it were written out in full.

NONSTANDARD   This answer *don't* look right to me. (don't = do not)
STANDARD   This answer **doesn't** look right to me. (doesn't = does not)

The same simple test works equally well with other contractions:

CONTRACTIONS   *isn't* (*is not*) and *aren't* (*are not*), *wasn't* (*was not*) and *weren't* (*were not*), *hasn't* (*has not*) and *haven't* (*have not*).

EXERCISE B   Underline the subject of each sentence and the verb in the parentheses that agrees with the subject. Be especially careful with contractions like *don't* and *doesn't*. (Add 10 points for each correct answer.)

1. My work (consists, consist) mainly of outdoor chores.

2. No, it just (doesn't, don't) seem right to me.

3. No one but Jacqueline (wants, want) to go.

4. The tomatoes (has, have) been doing especially well this year.

5. The garden (doesn't, don't) take as much work as I expected.

6. As I recall, you (wasn't, weren't) out for the team last year.

7. Some newspapers (doesn't, don't) print much foreign news.

8. My uncle (comes, come) to visit us every spring.

9. My grandparents (was, were) both born in 1901.

10. Morning glories (closes, close) up their flowers at night.

Problems with Prepositional Phrases

Many errors in subject-verb agreement occur in sentences in which a prepositional phrase comes between the subject and the verb.

The number of a subject is not changed by a prepositional phrase following the subject.

NONSTANDARD   A box of apples *were* shipped from Yakima.
NONSTANDARD   The shelves in the kitchen *needs* paint.

Unless our sentence sense is working full time, the phrase may make us forget what the subject of the sentence really is. We may then make the verb agree with a word in the phrase instead of with its subject, especially if the phrase begins with *of*. Remember, however, that the subject of a sentence is never found in a prepositional phrase. You can double-check the subject-verb agreement in sentences like these by mentally dropping out the phrase that follows the subject.

STANDARD   A box (of apples) was shipped from Yakima.

STANDARD   The shelves (in the kitchen) need paint.

EXERCISE A   Put parentheses around the prepositional phrases in the sentences below. Then underline the subject in each sentence and the verb in the parentheses that agrees with the subject. (Add 10 points for each correct sentence.)

A. The poems (in our literature book) (is, are) well chosen.

1. The descriptions in the poem about Paul Revere almost (makes, make) you forget where you are.

2. Many lines in the poem (is, are) especially good.

3. The tramp of feet (is, are) heard.

4. The hurrying hoofbeats of Paul Revere's horse (shatters, shatter) the silence.

5. The scenes on each village street (lives, live) again.

6. Many poems by Longfellow (has, have) effective descriptive passages.

7. One of my favorite poems (is, are) "Father William" by Lewis Carroll.

8. The antics of the old man always (makes, make) me laugh.

9. Some of the father's answers to his son (is, are) particularly amusing.

10. The father's reason for doing headstands (tickles, tickle) my funnybone.

EXERCISE B Circle the correct form of the verbs in parentheses in the paragraph below. (Add 10 points for each correct answer.)

THE PLANET MERCURY

1   The nearest to the sun of all the planets (was, were) named after the
2   Greek god Hermes. The name of the planet according to the Romans
3   (was, were) Mercury, and this is the name by which the people of today
4   (knows, know) the planet. Hermes, the swiftest of all the gods, (has,
5   have) been described as having winged sandals and a winged helmet.
6   Stories in mythology often (portrays, portray) him as the messenger of
7   the gods. Mail carriers in this country (uses, use) Hermes as the symbol
8   of their profession. The ancient Greeks noticed that one of the planets
9   (seems, seem) to move across the sky more swiftly than any other. They
10   decided that the swiftest one of the planets (was, were) to be named after
11   the swiftest of gods. Since then astronomers with improved equipment
12   (has, have) discovered planets other than the six known to the ancient
13   Greeks and (has, have) continued the tradtion of naming them after the
14   gods of Greek mythology.

Questions; THERE and HERE Sentences

Questions and other kinds of sentences may be turned about so that the subject comes after the verb. This arrangement of words in the sentence may lead to errors in the agreement between the subject and verb.

When the subject comes after the verb, be especially careful to determine the subject and make sure the verb agrees with it.

EXAMPLES Isn't Jean coming here this summer? (singular)

Does Anton want a new car? (singular)

Do the boys like oysters? (plural)

Aren't they in a hurry? (plural)

In sentences that begin with the words *here, there,* and *where,* the subject usually comes after the verb.

EXAMPLES Here are your pencils on my desk.

There are several bands in the parade.

Where were the students from our school?

If you are uncertain about whether to use a singular or a plural verb, you can determine which to use by changing the word order around so that the subject comes first.

EXAMPLE Your pencils are here on my desk.

Here's, there's, and *where's* are contractions of *here is, there is,* and *where is* and should be used only with singular subjects.

NONSTANDARD *Where's* my books? (Where is my books?)

STANDARD Where are my books?

STANDARD Where's my book?

EXERCISE Underline the subject in each uncompleted sentence and complete the sentence by filling the blank with the correct one of the two verbs in the parentheses. (Add 4 points for each correct sentence.)

A. (Does, Do) ....*Does*.... your father like picnics?

B. Where (is, are) ....*is*.... the soccer equipment kept?

1. Down the street (comes, come) .... the baton twirlers.

2. There (is, are) .... twenty students in my French class.

3. (Do, does) .... the member of the team practice?

173

4. Where (does, do) .... Miss Bannerman post the daily bulletin?

5. Here (is, are) .... the references you need for your history paper.

6. (Does, do) .... Mr. MacBain give many A's?

7. There (is, are) .... no ice skating on the pond unless the flag is up.

8. There (is, are) .... many varieties of oak tree.

9. (Has, Have) .... Amy asked anyone to the Sadie Hawkins dance?

10. Where (was, were) .... the receiver when he passed the ball?

11. (Do, Does) .... everyone here like pizza?

12. Here (is, are) .... the list of students who signed up to work on the play.

13. There (is, are) .... many mistakes in your homework, Pam.

14. Here (is, are) .... the scout leader with all the cookies you ordered.

15. (Isn't, Aren't) .... the Drama Club rehearsing in the auditorium?

16. Where (is, are) .... Stephen with the new uniforms?

17. There (is, are) .... a new family on our block.

18. (Do, Does) .... Emily Jones have a big dog?

19. There (is, are) .... lots of potholes in the street.

20. (Has, Have) .... the names of the winners been announced?

21. (Don't, Doesn't) .... it matter to you whether you go?

22. (Hasn't, Haven't) .... Andres passed his driving test?

23. Where (is, are) .... one of those sprayers that kill bugs?

24. (Was, Were) .... the boys going to cook supper for the girls?

25. Here (is, are) .... several of the books you were looking for.

Agreement with Pronouns

The subject and verb must agree when the subject is a pronoun. Besides the personal pronouns, there is a group of pronouns called *indefinite pronouns*. Some of these are singular in number, and others are plural.

The following pronouns are singular and take a singular verb: anybody, anyone, each, either, neither, everybody, everyone, nobody, no one, one, somebody, someone.

EXAMPLES Either is correct.

Everyone has been invited.

Watch out for the indefinite pronouns when they are separated from their verbs by a prepositional phrase or adjective clause.

EXAMPLES Either (of the answers) is correct.   (phrase)

Everyone (who attends our pottery classes) has been invited. (clause)

The following pronouns are plural and take plural verbs: both, few, many, several.

EXAMPLES Several (of my friends) play musical instruments.

Many (in the club) are not happy with the new rules.

EXERCISE A   Underline the correct form of the verb in the parentheses in each sentence. (Add 10 points for each correct answer.)

1. Anybody who is interested in boats (needs, need) to know how to swim.

2. Everyone in her classes (like, likes) Ms. Gobel.

3. Many of the group (prefers, prefer) to go to Paris.

4. Each of these shirts (costs, cost) four dollars.

5. Several in the eighth grade (wants, want) to have a class picnic in the spring.

6. Everyone in this group (has, have) a very definite preference.

7. Both of the maples in our front yard (turns, turn) red in the fall.

8. One of them (becomes, become) scarlet sooner than the others.

9. Neither of my grandmothers (is, are) living.

10. Few of the documents (was, were) authentic.

EXERCISE B Some of the following sentences contain errors in agreement between the subject and the verb. If the italicized verb is incorrect, cross it out and write the correct verb in the blank at the right. If the sentence is correct, write *C* in the blank. (Add 10 points for each correctly marked sentence.)

A. One of our visits *were* to the planetarium. A. *was*

1. Many of us *has* been fascinated by the wonders of outer space. 1. . . . .

2. Some in our class *is* looking toward the unknown with expectation. 2. . . . .

3. Not one of our astronomers *know* if life exists on planets in other solar systems. 3. . . . .

4. Neither the astronomers nor the physicists *is* sure whether we will encounter hospitable environments. 4. . . . .

5. Not everyone *want* to explore the unknown. 5. . . . .

6. Several among us *fears* that alien life forms may be hostile. 6. . . . .

7. A few of us *dream* of being among the first explorers of another galaxy. 7. . . . .

8. Every one of you *has* read a science fiction story at one time or another. 8. . . . .

9. Many of the authors *has* peopled the universe with unusual creatures. 9. . . . .

10. Several of the writers of science fiction *has* made predictions that have come true. 10. . . . .

Agreement with Compound Subjects

Subjects joined by <u>and</u> are plural and take a plural verb.

EXAMPLES Paula and her sister are hiking in Peru.

Two baseballs and a bat lay near home plate.

Boys and girls are washing the cars.

Singular subjects joined by <u>or</u> or <u>nor</u> are singular and take a singular verb.

The *or* or *nor* joining compound subjects means that one *or* the other—not both—is performing the action at a given time.

EXAMPLES Neither the book nor the magazine has the information.

Either the doctor or the nurse is coming.

Ice or sleet makes hills treacherous for driving.

Plural subjects joined by *or* or *nor* take a plural verb.

EXAMPLES The Perezes or the Petersons are taking us in their car.

Neither the boys nor the girls are winning in the district spelling tournament.

My brothers or their friends are going to give a party.

When a singular subject and a plural subject are joined by <u>or</u> or <u>nor</u>, the verb agrees with the subject nearer the verb.

EXAMPLES Either the two zebras or the giraffe has escaped from the lions.

Neither Marina nor her friends have missed karate class.

EXERCISE A Fill each blank with the correct one of the two verbs in parentheses. (Add 10 points for each correct answer.)

1. Carmen and Bob (has, have) offered to have the meeting at their house.
   1. . . . .

2. They and the Bellinis (lives, live) across the street from the school.
   2. . . . .

3. Jane and another committee member (has, have) already arrived.
   3. . . . .

4. Neither Al nor his brothers (is, are) able to be here.
   4. . . . .

5. Either Jane or Carmen (is, are) going to conduct the business meeting. 5. . . . .

6. Bob or Jane (reads, read) the treasurer's report when Al can't come. 6. . . . .

7. (Does, Do) Carmen and the other members get bored during the business meeting? 7. . . . .

8. The girls and boys (takes, take) turns bringing the refreshments. 8. . . . .

9. There (is, are) a carton of root beer or a box of cookies in the bag beside the sink. 9. . . . .

10. Usually Al and some of the others (comes, come) solely because of the refreshments. 10. . . . .

EXERCISE B Some of these sentences contain errors in agreement between the subject and the verb. Correct these errors by crossing out the incorrect form and putting the correct form in the blank at the right. If the sentence is correct, write *C* in the blank. (Add 10 points for each correctly marked sentence.)

1. Neither Henry nor Sam are able to help us today. 1. . . . .

2. Both Charlene and Irene have completed their work on the bulletin board. 2. . . . .

3. Kate, Ann, and Inez has monitor duty next week. 3. . . . .

4. Neither the cake nor the ice cream have been served yet. 4. . . . .

5. Neither John nor Wilfred is ever here more than a minute before the bell rings. 5. . . . .

6. Both Leroi and Margarita is interested in fishing. 6. . . . .

7. There's two trucks and an old car ahead of us. 7. . . . .

8. A pencil or a pen are necessary for filling out registration blanks. 8. . . . .

9. Janet or Bernadette goes to the student council meeting this morning. 9. . . . .

10. Either Pete or Fred have a watch with a sweep second hand. 10. . . . .

Chapter Review

EXERCISE A Fill each blank with the correct one of the two words in parentheses. (Add 5 points for each correct answer.)

1. (There's, There are) . . . . few potential leaders in this group.

2. Either Eugene or Jerry (is, are) . . . . destined to be Ed's successor.

3. Why (doesn't, don't) . . . . he ever come along with us?

4. Invariably there (was, were) . . . . some students who were more interested in writing than others.

5. Neither Ms. Columbo nor Mr. Andrews (was, were) . . . . able to tell where the trouble lay.

6. Their plan for the festivities (wasn't, weren't) . . . . very well thought out.

7. Each of the contestants (seems, seem) . . . . well qualified for the scholarship.

8. Both of the students (hopes, hope) . . . . to win the essay contest.

9. One of those drugstores (has, have) . . . . a big sale this week.

10. My brother (doesn't, don't) . . . . know that I have borrowed his tennis racket.

11. One of these bottles (contains, contain) . . . . suntan lotion.

12. (Does, Do) . . . . the pen and pencil come as a set?

13. Nobody in these stores (sells, sell) . . . . the kind of shoes I am looking for.

14. (Here's, Here are) . . . . two interesting articles in this magazine.

15. (There's, There are) . . . . now machines that translate foreign languages.

16. We (was, were) . . . . talking about these machines in French class.

17. One of the articles (is, are) . . . . about the letters of Abigail Adams.

18. Here (comes, come) . . . . Mother and Dad now.

19. You (wasn't, weren't) . . . . home when we telephoned.

20. There (isn't, aren't) . . . . any letters in the mailbox.

EXERCISE B Underline the subject once and the verb twice in each sentence. If there is an agreement error, draw a line through the incorrect verb and write the correct form in the space at the right. If the sentence is correct, write *C* in the blank. (Add 10 points for each correctly marked sentence.)

A. One of these books is about the sea. A. ..... *C* ....

B. Neither of the girls ~~have~~ the information. B. ... *has* .....

1. The effects of the long dry spell was disastrous for crops and cattle. 1. ....

2. There was too many swimmers at the pool. 2. ....

3. Here is two recipes for cookies without any chocolate. 3. ....

4. There is beauty in every facet of nature. 4. ....

5. Each of these books have some good descriptions. 5. ....

6. Towns and seaports were springing up. 6. ....

7. A wild tale of hidden riches were enough to start a bold expedition. 7. ....

8. One of the most daring mountain climbers was Annie Peck. 8. ....

9. Early explorations or pioneer adventures suggest many different topics for reports. 9. ....

10. Trade with other countries are important for our prosperity. 10. ....

180

Cumulative Review

A In each sentence, underline the word or words indicated in parentheses. (Add 5 points for each correct answer.)

1. Whenever in search of a worthwhile pastime, try picking up an appealing magazine. (adverb phrase)

2. Magazines for hobbyists and magazines about world events are published throughout the world in various formats. (four prepositional phrases)

3. Hours can be spent thumbing through magazines in a library before a reader gets bored. (adverb clause)

4. A pile of magazines beside the bed often makes the day more pleasant for someone who is ill. (three prepositional phrases)

5. After someone is through with a magazine, it's a good idea to pass it on to someone else. (adverb clause)

6. When magazines are shared, it's easy for everyone in a group of friends to catch up on news, sports, fashion, culture, and politics. (adverb clause)

7. The regular reader of magazines gains much knowledge. (direct object)

8. Magazine photography is a fascinating subject for research. (subject complement)

9. Margaret Bourke-White was a magazine photographer who worked during World War II. (adjective clause)

10. She flew on combat missions and survived the torpedoing of a ship. (adverb phrase)

11. In Europe she took many pictures of battle scenes. (direct object)

12. After the war Margaret continued to take pictures that thrilled magazine readers. (adjective clause)

13. She once photographed a jet airplane breaking the sound barrier. (adverb)

14. Her book *Portrait of Myself* contains many of the photographs that she took for magazines over her long career. (adjective clause)

15. Weekly magazines and other periodicals which contain her photography are now collectors' items. (compound subject)

B Add punctuation marks and capital letters wherever they are needed in each of the following sentences. (Add 10 points for each correct sentence.)

1. "I received a letter from Heather today said Roy shes in san diego.

2. Whats she doing there, asked beth.

3. Oh, didnt I tell you questioned Roy. "Shes traveling with a bus and truck company for *dames at sea.*

4. Beth asked a bus and what company? I have to hear about this

5. A bus and truck company travels around the country doing a show explained Roy

6. He added when the show closes in one town, they pack all the costumes and props in the truck and all the cast in the bus and set off to a new town."

7. Thats really exciting exclaimed Beth. What role does Heather play.

8. "She plays Mona, the vamp, said Roy actually shes quite good too.

9. Beth asked Will we be able to see the show will it play around here somewhere?

10. It will be in seattle for two weeks in august perhaps we can see it then, suggested Roy.

Building Vocabulary: Explaining What Words Stand For

In order to talk about horses, we do not have to lead around with us the four-legged animal which is called a horse. We merely say the word *horse,* and people know what kind of thing we are talking about.

The word *horse* stands for the animal. Many of the words we use stand for things (*lamp, car, book*) or actions (*run, talk, climb*) that we can experience physically. We know the meaning of such words because we have experienced the things or actions for which they stand. In much the same way we also learn the meaning of words that stand for ideas (*courage, justice, freedom*) or qualities (*ugly, angry, intelligent*). Often, the best way to understand and explain such words is to tell about the things they stand for.

Many words can be defined by describing what they stand for or by giving examples.

EXAMPLE   Mushrooms are an edible fungus, but toadstools are not edible.

Here, we are explaining the meaning of *edible* by *giving examples.* Mushrooms are a food, that is, *fit to eat.* Toadstools are *not edible* (in*edible*), that is, *not fit to eat* (because they are poisonous).

We can explain a word that stands for a physical object or an action by describing the object or by telling how the action is performed. Notice how the noun *caption* and the verb *to bask* are explained in these examples.

OBJECT   A caption is the written explanation that is printed beneath a picture in a book, magazine, or newspaper.

ACTION   To bask, one lies or sits in pleasantly warm sunlight and soaks up the warmth.

As you read the following definitions, decide whether each word is explained by means of an example or by a description of the object or action for which it stands.

allusion /ə lū́ zhən/, *n.* The expression "render unto Caesar . . ." is an *allusion,* or brief reference to the Bible, while "to be or not to be" is an *allusion* to Shakespeare's play *Hamlet.*

compromise /kóm prə mīz/, *v.* To *compromise* in reaching an agreement, both sides must give in on some points so that the result is acceptable to both.

cove /kōv/, *n.* A *cove* is an inlet in a coastline with high land around it, suitable for anchoring boats in; a small, sheltered bay.

crag /krag/, *n.* A *crag* is a steep, rough mass of rock that rises above or sticks out from the mountain of which it is a part.

cumulus /kyū́m yə ləs/, *n* A *cumulus,* or *cumulus cloud,* is a wide, high, piled-up, rounded mass of white cloud.

decipher /di sī́ fər/, *v.* One *deciphers* a message written in a code, or *cipher,* by changing it into ordinary language. Loosely, one may be said to *decipher* anything, such as poor handwriting or a confusing statement, that is hard to understand.

dissonant /dís ə nənt/, *adj.* Musical notes

183

too close together to harmonize are *dissonant*. The sounds of an orchestra tuning up, with no instruments playing together, are *dissonant*. The harsh machine noises of an assembly line would be called *dissonant*.

fossil /fós əl/, *n*. Rock dug from the earth and having on or in it the mark or shape of any prehistoric living thing is called a *fossil*.

jargon /jár gon/, *n*. Outsiders are not likely to understand the *jargon* in which scientists, artists, or doctors discuss their profession with one another. The special vocabulary made up to meet the needs of a trade or profession is called *jargon*.

sumptuous /súmp chū əs/, *adj*. The banquet of a Roman emperor, which would impress one by its luxury and great costliness, would be called *sumptuous*. A movie star often lives in *sumptuous* surroundings.

EXERCISE In each blank, write the word from this lesson that makes the best sense. In the space at the left write *E* if the word was explained above by means of *examples,* or *D* if the thing or action for which the word stands was *described.* (Add 5 points for each correct answer.)

.... 1. They rowed the boat to a small, sheltered . . . . where they decided to ground the boat and swim for a while.

.... 2. . . . . clouds are usually seen on a warm, sunny summer day.

.... 3. The title of the newspaper editorial was a(n) . . . . to the Bill of Rights.

.... 4. Lynn has sent the . . . . that she found in Colorado to the Museum of Natural History.

.... 5. In the peculiar . . . . of the sports writer, Annette had "hooped" two more points in the final minutes of the game.

.... 6. The printers and the publishers would not . . . . , and as a result New York City had no newspapers for more than three months.

.... 7. At midnight, the . . . . banging of pans, hooting of whistles, and ringing of bells ushered in the New Year.

.... 8. At the top of a distant . . . ., outlined against the setting sun, a mountain goat stood motionless.

.... 9. Our ability to . . . . enemy messages was a great advantage to the United States during World War II.

.... 10. A party need not be . . . . for the guests to have a good time.

Spelling: Homophones

Many spelling errors result from confusing pairs (or trios) of words that *sound* exactly alike but differ in spelling as well as meaning. Clear articulation and correct pronunciation won't help you to spell such words, which are called *homophones*. The only way to master *homophones* is to learn their spelling and meaning *together*. If you can keep in mind a set of short model sentences in which both spelling and meaning stand out for you, you can conquer most homophones.

Try to memorize the common trouble-making homophones below:

born	Hiroto was **born** in Japan.
borne	We had **borne** their insults patiently.
compliment	Mom gave Beatrice a **compliment** on her good marks.
complement	Your talents will **complement** his.
fare	Pay your fifty-cent **fare**, please.
fair	Your demand is not **fair**. Let's go to the county **fair**.
miner	Dan was a coal **miner**.
minor	That is a **minor** point. You are a **minor** until you reach legal age.
peace	The dove is a symbol of **peace**.
piece	Have a **piece** of cake.
plain	He has a **plain** face. Level ground is called a **plain**.
plane	We heard a **plane** overhead. Hand me the **plane** and saw.
soul	The boy sang with all his heart and **soul**.
sole	She was the **sole** survivor. The **sole** of my foot hurts.
there	**There** is no excuse. Look over **there**!
their	The farmers put down **their** rakes.
they're	**They're** late right now.
waist	She has a tiny **waist**.
waste	Don't **waste** your breath.
whose	**Whose** lunch is this?
who's	**Who's** going to the beach?

EXERCISE A Underline the correct word from each pair in parentheses. (Add 10 points for each correct answer.)

1. I don't believe every (compliment, complement) I hear.

2. When (there, they're) all baked, you may have some cupcakes.

3. Our family prefers (plain, plane) cooking.

4. Timothy is his father's (soul, sole) heir.

5. He was a (miner, minor) poet of little fame.

6. All your predictions have been (born, borne) out.

7. That's just not (fare, fair).

8. Most people want (peace, piece), if possible.

9. Do you know (whose, who's) coming to the concert?

10. It's foolish to (waist, waste) time.

EXERCISE B   In the blank to the left of each meaning in column *1* below, write the letter (*a, b, c,* etc.) of the appropriate word from column *2*. (Add 10 points for each correct answer.)

	1		*2*	
. . .	1. the opposite of war	a. fare	i. waist	
. . .	2. the middle part of the body	b. peace	j. fair	
. . .	3. the opposite of fancy	c. waste	k. soul	
. . .	4. one who digs for ore, coal, metal	d. miner	l. piece	
. . .	5. brought into existence by birth	e. plain	m. plane	
. . .	6. the under part of the foot or shoe	f. compliment	n. minor	
. . .	7. the cost of transportation	g. sole	o. complement	
. . .	8. to give praise	h. borne	p. born	
. . .	9. not of legal age			
. . .	10. a vehicle for air travel			

REVIEW EXERCISE   Be prepared to write the following words from dictation. (Add 10 points for each correctly spelled word.)

1. candidate
2. quantity
3. sixth
4. temperature
5. recognize
6. whisper
7. government
8. congratulate
9. probably
10. width

CHAPTER TEN

Using Verbs Correctly

Verbs express action, and action takes place in time—yesterday, today, tomorrow. When we use a verb, it is usually important to show just when the action takes place. We do this, mostly without thinking about it, by means of adverbs, helping verbs, and by certain changes in the verbs themselves. Most verbs express time in much the same ways, but the few that express time in different ways cause no end of trouble. It is with these few *irregular verbs* that we shall mainly concern ourselves in this chapter.

LESSON 93

Past, Present, and Future

A verb expresses changes in time by varying its *tense*. All the tenses of a verb are put together from four basic forms called the *principal parts*.

The principal parts of a verb are the present, the present participle, the past, and the past participle.

PRESENT	PRESENT PARTICIPLE	PAST	PAST PARTICIPLE
call	calling	called	(have) called
laugh	laughing	laughed	(have) laughed
bake	baking	baked	(have) baked

Regular verbs form the past and past participle by adding –ed or –d to the present form.

The past participle is used with the helping verb *have, has,* or *had* to form the perfect tenses, that show action which took place in the past.

EXAMPLES   Virginia has played the clarinet.
She had called Emily about it.

The present participle of *all* verbs is always formed by adding *–ing* to the present form of the verb. It is used with the helping verb *to be* (am, is, are—was, were—been).

EXAMPLES   I am trying to study.
We were planning a surprise for Dad.

187

EXERCISE A In the spaces provided, write the two missing principal parts of each of the following regular verbs. (Add 5 points for each correct answer.)

Present	Present Part.	Past	Past Part.
1.	believing	believed	....
2. shout	shouting	....	....
3. ask	....	asked	....
4. like	liking	....	....
5.	....	climbed	climbed
6.	working	....	worked
7.	smiling	....	smiled
8. follow	....	followed	....
9.	....	supported	supported
10.	completing	....	completed

EXERCISE B Fill in the correct principal part of the verb in parentheses —the present, the past, or the past participle—depending on the meaning of the sentence. (Add 10 points for each correct answer.)

1. Our city is (sponsor) .... an energy conservation campaign.

2. At school, we (hear) .... a speech about how to cut down on the use of fuel.

3. Mr. Thompson, the custodian, has (turn) .... the thermostat down to 65 degrees (18 C).

4. Half the light bulbs in the hallways have been (remove) ....

5. We are (turn) .... off lights when we leave the room.

6. My mother has (change) .... the temperature of the water heater to a lower setting.

7. We (close) .... the valve of the radiator in the guest room and shut the door.

8. People with greenhouses are (gain) .... heat from the trapped sunlight.

9. Many citizens are (purchase) .... wood-burning stoves too.

10. I think we have (achieve) .... progress in energy conservation.

Irregular Verbs

Although most verbs form their past tenses by adding *-ed* or *-d* to the present, some verbs do not follow this rule.

An irregular verb does not form its past and past participle by adding –ed or –d to the present form.

The verbs *see, do, come,* and *go* are used so often that it is important to know their correct forms. Because the past and past participle forms do not follow any rules, they must be memorized. The present participle is always formed by adding *-ing* to the present (seeing, doing, coming, going).

PRESENT	PAST	PAST PARTICIPLE
see	saw	(have) seen
do	did	(have) done
come	came	(have) come
go	went	(have) gone

Whenever you are memorizing the parts of an irregular verb, you can practice by following a pattern of three sentences such as the following:

PRESENT Today I **see** him.   Today I **go** to school.
PAST   Yesterday I **saw** him.   Yesterday I **went** to school.
PERFECT Often I <u>have seen</u> him. Often I <u>have gone</u> to school.

It is incorrect in standard English to use the past participle without a helping verb.

NONSTANDARD   I *seen* that movie.   We *done* our work.
STANDARD   I <u>have</u> seen that movie. We <u>have</u> done our work.

The past form of these verbs should never be used with a helping verb.

NONSTANDARD   Doug and Salvatore *have went* home.
              They *have came* for a visit.
STANDARD   Doug and Salvatore <u>went</u> home.
              They <u>came</u> for a visit.

EXERCISE A Fill in the blank in each sentence with the correct past form of the verb in parentheses. (Add 5 points for each correct answer.)

1. Paul (do) . . . . his homework last night.

2. We (see) . . . . Ann's poster in art class.

3. Have you (go) . . . . to the library already?

4. We (come) . . . . past there before school.

5. I had (go) .... to school early.

6. I (see) .... Ed on the way.

7. What a good job Jacob (do) .... on his poster!

8. You (see) .... his poster, didn't you?

9. Time has (go) .... so fast.

10. We should have (come) .... to school earlier.

11. I (do) .... only four of these problems.

12. Have you (see) .... my pencil?

13. Until now, I have not (go) .... to class unprepared.

14. I should have (do) .... this work last night.

15. Unexpected guests (come) .... over.

16. My parents had (go) .... shopping.

17. As they (come) .... home, our friends arrived.

18. We had not (see) .... our friends for a long time.

19. After they left, I (do) .... my English assignment.

20. I (come) .... to school early today to finish my math.

EXERCISE B Underline the correct one of two verbs in parentheses. (Add 10 points for each correct answer.)

1. If you have (did, done) your best, that is all that matters.

2. We (have come, come) a long way to be here tonight.

3. Have they (saw, seen) your new guitar yet?

4. Rose Marie and Janice (gone, went) shopping.

5. The Sunday newspaper has not (came, come) yet.

6. Has he (did, done) what he promised to do?

7. The girls on the ball team (came, come) early yesterday.

8. We (seen, saw) her earlier this morning.

9. Have you (went, gone) to have your picture taken yet?

10. My aunt and uncle have (came, come) for dinner.

Sixteen Irregular Verbs

Many irregular verbs are irregular in similar ways. Memorize the principal parts of these verbs so that you can write them when someone names the present form of each verb. If you use the helping verb *have* when learning the past participle, you will not confuse it with the past.

PRESENT	PAST	PAST PARTICIPLE
begin	began	(have) begun
drink	drank	(have) drunk
swim	swam	(have) swum
run	ran	(have) run
break	broke	(have) broken
speak	spoke	(have) spoken
choose	chose	(have) chosen
freeze	froze	(have) frozen
drive	drove	(have) driven
ride	rode	(have) ridden
write	wrote	(have) written
take	took	(have) taken
throw	threw	(have) thrown
know	knew	(have) known
grow	grew	(have) grown
bring	brought	(have) brought

The last verb on the list, *bring,* does not fit in with any of the other patterns. There are no such words as *brang, brung,* or *broughten.* The past and past participle of *bring* are both the same—*brought.*

EXERCISE A   Fill in the blank with the correct past form of the verb in parentheses. Remember that the past participle must be used with any form of the helping verb *to have.* (Add 4 points for each correct answer.)

1. Laura, have you (bring) .... your tennis racket?

2. Yesterday Donna (choose) .... you as her partner.

3. Have you (take) .... any pictures yet, Ilona?

4. Without my jacket I have nearly (freeze) .... today.

5. The Tarbelles have (begin) .... to build a cabin next to ours.

6. Our little kitten has (drink) .... all its milk.

7. Have you (speak) .... to Eva about our picnic?

8. Mother has already (write) .... to Aunt Helen.

191

9. Willis, have you (throw) .... away all the old newspapers?

10. I (know) .... Sean Callahan in grade school.

11. A plate was (break) .... when we moved.

12. We have (drive) .... on this highway before.

13. Have you ever (ride) .... in an airplane?

14. Victoria Woodhull (run) .... for President in 1872.

15. Yesterday we (swim) .... to the du Bois raft.

16. We (bring) .... our lunch to school.

17. Have you (choose) .... your committee, George?

18. We (drink) .... all the lemonade.

19. I have (know) .... Mae Wing for several years.

20. Who (throw) .... this notebook in the wastebasket?

21. The milk has (freeze) .... in the bottles.

22. Have you ever (swim) .... across Mirror Lake?

23. I would have been on time if I hadn't (break) .... my watch.

24. Theresa (choose) .... to take French instead of Spanish.

25. They have already (begin) .... the meeting.

EXERCISE B Irregular verbs from this lesson are printed in italics in the paragraph below. Draw a line through any italicized verb which is used incorrectly and write the correct verb form above it. Some of the italicized verbs are correct. Write *C* above the correct verbs. (Add 10 points for each correct answer.)

CAMPING OUT

1 As it *began* ~~begun~~ to get dark, I *brung* my sleeping bag closer to the fire and

2 unrolled it. Then I *took* the pail down to the stream and filled it. I *drunk*

3 from the same clear mountain stream in which I had *swam* earlier in

4 the day. Only yesterday, I had *rode* up from the valley with my Shoshoni

5 friend Henry Feather, who *ran* the outfitting service at Jackson. I felt

6 extremely remote from my everyday life at home. I had come by train

7 as far as Jackson. Then we *had drove* by jeep to the Dugan ranch and

8 *had rode* from there. I *knowed* I would have much to tell my parents

9 when I next *wrote* to them.

Using SIT and SET Correctly

The verb sit means to sit down, to occupy a seat, or to be in place.

PRESENT	PRESENT PARTICIPLE	PAST	PAST PARTICIPLE
sit	sitting	sat	(have) sat

EXAMPLES We always sit on the thirty-yard line. (present)

I had never sat on such an uncomfortable seat. (past participle)

The food is sitting on the table. (present participle)

How long were you sitting there? (present participle)

The verb *sit* does not ordinarily take a direct object.

The verb set means to place or to put something down.

PRESENT	PRESENT PARTICIPLE	PAST	PAST PARTICIPLE
set	setting	set	(have) set

EXAMPLES I set the *pan* on the stove and forgot about it. (past)

I am setting my *purse* where I won't forget it. (present participle)

The chef has set the *cake* in the middle of the table. (past participle)

Notice that *set* is followed by an object in the examples. *Set* usually takes an object. *Sit* does not.

EXERCISE A In the space at the left, write *S* if the verb in parentheses must mean *to sit*, *P* if it must mean *to put* (*something*). Your answer will depend on the meaning of the sentence. Then underline the correct verb form. (Add 5 points for each correct sentence.)

... S ... A. The cat has been (sitting, setting) on the roof all day.

.... 1. How long has that child been (sitting, setting) on the steps?

.... 2. I will (sit, set) the pan back on the stove.

.... 3. Has this clock been (sitting, setting) on the mantel all the time?

.... 4. We (sat, set) with Frank on the bus yesterday morning.

.... 5. Dorothy Hamill (sat, set) her skates on the bench.

.... 6. I have (sat, set) here for an hour reading this book.

.... 7. We were (sitting, setting) at our desks when Mr. McGovern came in.

.... 8. Ernesto has (sat, set) in this same seat all semester.

.... 9. Chris will (sit, set) in the front row and listen intently.

.... 10. Shall we (sit, set) here and wait for Hector?

.... 11. My brother accidentally (sat, set) on his glasses.

.... 12. Please (sit, set) that piano down.

.... 13. The bus driver (sat, set) and waited for us.

.... 14. Unless you (sit, set) down, we cannot begin.

.... 15. The mail carrier has (sat, set) the magazines on the porch chair.

.... 16. There is no one I know (sitting, setting) in the bleachers.

.... 17. Have you ever (sat, set) under a willow tree in the summer?

.... 18. We were supposed to (sit, set) the forks next to the knives.

.... 19. Meg was (sitting, setting) pies out to cool.

.... 20. Nat has (sat, set) the words to music.

EXERCISE B   Fill each blank with the correct form of *sit* or *set*. (Add 10 points for each correct answer.)

1   Bob was .... the tables in his luncheonette when several

2   young people came in and .... down at the counter. They

3   .... their school books on the floor next to the counter. "Why

4   not .... your books by the window?" asked Bob. After stor-

5   ing their books, the students .... on the stools and talked

6   quietly among themselves. Bob came around the counter and

7   .... down on the end stool. He looked at his watch, and then

8   at the clock by the kitchen door. "I must have fogotten to ....

9   my watch," he thought. "Who .... you people free at 2:00?"

10   he asked the student next to him.

11   "The air-conditioning system broke down," explained one student,

12   "so the principal let us out a little early."

13   "Well, don't just .... there," Bob laughed. "Order some-

14   thing!" He quickly .... menus in front of them.

194

Using LIE and LAY Correctly

The verb lie means to lie down or to rest in a flat position.

PRESENT	PRESENT PARTICIPLE	PAST	PAST PARTICIPLE
lie	lying	lay	(have) lain

EXAMPLES Grandmother lies down every afternoon. (present)
Your coat is lying on my bed. (present participle)
Yesterday I lay in the sun for fifteen minutes. (past)
If I had lain there longer, I would have been sunburned. (past participle)

The verb *lie* does not ordinarily take a direct object.

The verb lay means to put something down.

PRESENT	PRESENT PARTICIPLE	PAST	PAST PARTICIPLE
lay	laying	laid	(have) laid

EXAMPLES Cynthia always lays the *mail* on the desk. (present)

I laid the *mail* on the kitchen table today. (past)

The workers are laying the *lumber* in piles. (present participle)

Have they laid *all* of it in piles? (past participle)

Remember: Although the verb *lay* generally has a direct object, the verb *lie* ordinarily does not have an object.

EXERCISE A In the space at the left, write *L* if the verb in parentheses must mean *to lie down*, *P* if it must mean *to put something down*. Then underline the correct verb form. (Add 10 points for each correct sentence.)

L. A. The lifeguard was (lying, laying) on the raft.

.... 1. Buster is (lying, laying) on the mat on the front porch.

.... 2. Jerry, you may (lie, lay) the blanket on the grass.

.... 3. The children (lay, laid) on the beach after their swim.

.... 4. I'll (lie, lay) this green rug in front of my dresser.

.... 5. The rake is (lying, laying) on the grass in the rain.

.... 6. The other tools have (lain, laid) in the garage all week.

.... 7. Workers are (lying, laying) the new linoleum.

.... 8. Alice has (lain, laid) the book on the librarian's desk.

.... 9. I just (lay, laid) the paper on the table.

.... 10. You should (lie, lay) down for a short rest, Pat.

EXERCISE B Fill each blank with the correct form of *lie* or *lay*. (Add 5 points for each correct answer.)

A. Your dog is .. *lying* ... in a bed of violets.

1. Rusty .... down and fell asleep on the sofa.

2. Your notebook was .... on the table when I came home.

3. If you .... your hands on my paintbox again, you'll regret it!

4. The workers had .... the foundation for the new school.

5. The fish was .... on its side in the tank.

6. A Rhode Island Red usually .... brown eggs.

7. After the treaty was signed, the soldiers .... down their arms.

8. Estella had just .... down when the doorbell rang.

9. Harry's books are .... on the floor again.

10. I will .... the blanket over her carefully so she won't wake up.

11. After the hurricane many boats were found .... on dry land.

12. The mason had .... the bricks for the post office.

13. I .... my notebook on the steps while we were talking.

14. It .... there all night in the rain.

15. On Tenth Street they are .... new storm sewers.

16. Olivia, who is supposed to cut the grass, is .... in the hammock.

17. Please .... your packages on the table.

18. Yesterday I .... on the beach all morning.

19. We had .... aside our work for a while.

20. I had .... in bed too long.

BRING or TAKE? LEAVE or LET?

The meanings of the verbs *bring* and *take* are quite different. Unless you are careful to use them correctly, you may find yourself saying the opposite of what you intended.

Use bring to show movement toward the speaker.

Bring means "to come carrying something." Think of *bring* as related to *come.*

EXAMPLES   Carmen, please **bring** me a pair of scissors.
You **brought** me the wrong pair.

Use take to show movement away from the speaker.

Take means "to go carrying something." Think of *take* as related to *go.*

EXAMPLES   Ann, please **take** these scissors to Carmen.
You **took** the wrong pair to her.

Review the principal parts of these two verbs before doing the exercise.

PRESENT	PRESENT PARTICIPLE	PAST	PAST PARTICIPLE
bring (to speaker)	bringing	brought	(have) brought
take (from speaker)	taking	took	(have) taken

EXERCISE A   Underline the correct verb in the parentheses. (Add 10 points for each correct answer.)

1. Please (bring, take) this package to the post office when you go.

2. Has the mail carrier (brought, taken) any mail to us today?

3. Seth, will you (bring, take) this magazine to the Martins?

4. They (brought, took) it here by mistake.

5. Julie, you'd better (bring, take) these books back to the library.

6. You should have (brought, taken) them back there yesterday.

7. John went to the beach and (brought, took) his model boat with him.

8. We are waiting for the deliverer to (bring, take) the groceries to us.

9. When he went to the game, Geoge (brought, took) me a sweater.

10. Sandy (brought, took) his bike downtown to the repair shop.

The verb leave means to depart, to go away, or to keep something where it is.

PRESENT	PRESENT PARTICIPLE	PAST	PAST PARTICIPLE
leave	leaving	left	(have) left

EXAMPLES   We left early for the ball game.

I must have left my library book at school.

The verb let means to allow or to permit.

PRESENT	PRESENT PARTICIPLE	PAST	PAST PARTICIPLE
let	letting	let	(have) let

Except for the present participle, *let* does not change its form.

EXAMPLES   Our parents let (not *left*) us make candy last night.   (past)

Please let (not *leave*) me have a piece.   (present)

When you mean *allow* or *permit*, always use *let*, not *leave*.

EXERCISE B   Underline the correct verb in the parentheses. (Add 10 points for each correct answer.)

1. My parents will (leave, let) me go with you.

2. James (left, let) his baseball at home.

3. (Leave, Let) him play anyway, Mike.

4. I had (left, let) Aretha borrow my bicycle.

5. Judy (left, let) me use hers.

6. We (left, let) everything in order.

7. Our parents are (leaving, letting) us plan another party.

8. We (left, let) the light burn all night in the hall.

9. I (left, let) the light burning on the porch.

10. No one should (leave, let) a child cross the street alone.

Chapter Review

EXERCISE A   In sentences 1–5, fill in each blank with the correct form of either *sit* or *set*. (Add 5 points for each correct answer.)

1. When Cindy practiced guitar, she often .... a metronome beside her.

2. Some people were .... on the floor.

3. Often she .... on a stool in front of a music stand.

4. Usually friends .... and listened to her play.

5. After an hour of playing, Cindy .... out refreshments.

In sentences 6–10, fill in each blank with the correct form of either *lie* or *lay*.

6. Our dog Maxwell always .... on the back porch.

7. Every morning he .... his rubber bone on the porch and then proceeds to block the doorway.

8. When we try to get by, he just .... there and looks at us.

9. Sometimes he lifts his head and then .... it down again.

10. He has .... by the door ever since I can remember.

In sentences 11–15, fill in each blank with the correct form of *leave* or *let*.

11. I believe schools should .... students have more responsibility for their behavior.

12. They must .... the principles of democracy function.

13. If they .... students to themselves, the students would learn to function as members of a democratic society.

14. Some people take the attitude that you can't change society, so you should .... it be.

15. Others feel that you can't .... decisions up to others, but you should take an active role in making them.

In sentences 16–20, fill in each blank with the correct form of *bring* or *take*.

16. Buffy .... me my father's slippers this morning.

17. She has .... all of my shoes to my parents' room.

18. We have tried to train her to .... us the newspaper.

19. Instead, she picks it up off the porch and .... it to her dog-house.

20. Poor Buffy! Every day she .... me her favorite bone.

EXERCISE B If an italicized verb in the following material is correct, write C above it. If it is incorrect, cross it out and write the correct form of the verb above it. (Add 5 points for each correct answer.)

WEATHER SIGNS

1   Even before people *knew* the laws of meteorology, they studied the
2   sky for indications of the coming weather. If they *seen* a red sky at night,
3   they considered it an omen for fair weather the next day. Another sign
4   that good weather would *come* was a clear, bright sky loaded with stars.
5   But if the day *begun* with a red sky, travelers *took* warning that the
6   weather would be unfavorable by afternoon.

7   Many people have *wrote* about the moon. According to these writers,
8   the moon is *known* to affect not only the weather but the lives of people
9   as well. If at night people *saw* films of clouds around the moon, they
10   would expect a storm by morning. A brilliant white moon that emitted
11   light for miles was *took* as an indication of clear weather. Halos and
12   coronas around the moon were *spoke* of as signs of storms.

13   A day that *begun* with a rainbow in the morning *brought* bad weather
14   by afternoon. Morning rainbows were *knowed* to come before a storm.
15   Rainbows in the afternoon *came* after a storm. They indicated enough
16   clearing in the sky to guarantee fair weather. Another factor that was
17   *taken* as a sign of bad weather was thunder in the morning.

18   Sailors who had *went* to sea *knew* that the winds heralded the weather.
19   A west wind meant fair weather whereas a northwest wind meant fair
20   weather accompanied by a cool breeze. No sailor who had nearly *froze*
21   to death while keeping watch could forget the meaning of a northeast
22   wind. In summer it *brung* cool, chilling rains, and in winter blizzards
23   and ice storms *came* with it.

Cumulative Review

A Identify the italicized words by writing one of the following abbreviations above each: *subj.* (subject), *v.* (verb), *o.p.* (object of preposition), *d.o.* (direct object), *s.c.* (subject complement). (Add 5 points for each correct answer.)

1   *We* built a bird *feeder* outside our kitchen *window*. There were *seeds*

2   and suet to please all *kinds* of birds. The *sparrows* were the *first* to discover

3   the feeder. There are certainly many *kinds* of sparrows. We were surprised

4   to find a song sparrow in the *winter*. Soon a *cardinal found* the *feeder*

5   and told the *rest* of the birds with its cheery *whistle*. It gave me a *thrill*

6   to see the birds so close. The chickadees and juncos are *neat* in their

7   gray and black costumes. The aggressive blue jays *chase* away the other

8   *birds*. The *birds* eat the *seeds* so quickly that we have to put out new

9   food every day.

B Underline the subordinate clause in each sentence. In the blank at the left, write *adj.* for an adjective clause or *adv.* for an adverb clause. (Add 10 points for each correct sentence.)

.... 1. The birds which I like the least are the starlings and the grackles.

.... 2. When I turned on the kitchen light late one night, I saw a snowy owl sitting on the feeder.

.... 3. It did not stay where it was for long.

.... 4. Soon it flew away because the light frightened it.

.... 5. There is only one other person in our town who has seen a snowy owl.

.... 6. He is an ex-soldier who was stationed in Alaska.

.... 7. Birdwatching is a pastime which many people enjoy.

.... 8. Perhaps the birds that are being watched enjoy watching the people, too.

.... 9. Although I have looked for a woodpecker, I haven't seen one.

.... 10. There must be one out there somewhere, however, because I can hear it at work.

C Punctuate and capitalize these sentences where necessary. (Add 20 points for each correctly marked numbered item.)

1. When I got on the bus this morning Mrs. Ball said, Sit down. I want to talk to you."

2. Have I done anything wrong I asked. I didn't think I had but one never knows.

3. Heavens, no, she laughed. "I have a niece named Elizabeth Ball, who lives in Orangeburg South carolina. She is coming for a visit, and I'd like her to meet some girls her own age. Since I am away at work most of the day it would be nice if she could be included in some of the girls activities."

4. "Id like to help Mrs. Ball," I said. When is she coming?

5. "Next wednesday, april twenty-seventh. Well, here is the county courthouse where I get off," Mrs. Ball said. Ill telephone you Jennie."

D Underline the correct one of the two words in the parentheses. (Add 10 points for each correct answer.)

A BASEBALL PICNIC

1   Mrs. Ball gave some tennis tickets to Elizabeth and (I, me). (We, Us)
2   girls are very fond of tennis. Either Amy or Lynn (was, were) talking about
3   this very match just the other day. Maybe they could come with (she, her)
4   and (I, me). Amy and Lynn (is, are) delighted to have a chance to go. A
5   few of (we, us) girls (is, are) planning to take along a picnic lunch. Amy
6   and I (is, are) going to pack a lunch for Liz. "You and (I, me) are going to
7   have my superduper sandwiches," Amy told Liz.

Building Vocabulary: Exact Definition

For many words, making an exact definition is a two-step process: (1) We must show how the word is similar in meaning to other words; and (2) we must show how the word differs in meaning. The second step is especially important. To use words correctly, you need to know not just their general meaning but how they differ from near synonyms.

To define a word, first relate it to other words that are close in meaning. Then show how it differs in meaning from these words.

EXAMPLE   Maureen galloped into the corral on a handsome roan.

From the context, *roan* must mean some kind of horse, but what kind exactly? How does the word *roan* differ in meaning from the more general word *horse,* which applies to all kinds of horses?

DEFINITION   A roan is a horse that is brown in color, with white or gray markings.

The definition tells us (1) that a roan is a kind of horse, and (2) that it is a particular kind of horse—a horse that is "brown in color, with white or gray markings."

EXERCISE A   In the following definitions: (1) put parentheses [( )] around the general word(s) that are similar in meaning to the word printed in red; and (2) underline the remaining words, which show how the word defined differs in meaning from its synonym(s). (Add 10 points for each correctly marked definition.)

A. adjourn /ə júrn/, *v.* (To end a meeting) with the intention of continuing it at a later time.

1. compensation /kóm pən sā shən/, *n.* Payment in money or goods in return for some service or to make up for an injury.

2. confiscate /kón fis kāt/, *v.* To take someone's money or property by government or other authority, as a punishment.

3. deficient /di físh ənt/, *adj.* Imperfect or defective because lacking in something necessary for completeness.

4. fantasy /fán tə sē/, *n.* A daydream; also, a story that is like a daydream, fanciful and wholly imaginary.

5. impulsive /im púl siv/, *adj.* Hasty; acting or behaving on *impulse,* a sudden, unthinking wish or desire.

6. orbit /áur bit/, *n.* The path taken by a heavenly body or an artificial satellite as it travels around another body.

203

7. **reef** /rēf/, *n.* An underwater ridge of rock that rises to near the surface of the water.

8. **scour** /skour/, *v.* To clean by rubbing hard.

9. **taunt** /taunt/, *v.* To jeer at; to attack with spiteful, insulting words.

10. **tyranny** /tír ə nē/, *n.* Government by a single, unjust ruler who is not responsible to the people.

EXERCISE B In each blank, write the word from this lesson that makes the best sense in the context. (Add 10 points for each correct answer.)

1. The satellite remained in . . . . for seven months.

2. The movers promised . . . . for the damage to our furniture.

3. We had to . . . . the pan for half an hour to get it clean.

4. During the storm, the ship struck a(n) . . . . and sank.

5. Predictions of space travel were once thought pure . . . .

6. I thought Melvin's behavior was . . . . in courtesy.

7. A(n) . . . . person, Mr. Poe often does things for no good reason.

8. The class was in an uproar until Miss Sydney was able to . . . . Herman's peashooter.

9. The French Revolution was fought to overthrow the . . . . of the monarchy.

10. It is absurd to . . . . someone for being different from us.

REVIEW EXERCISE Answer each question by writing *Yes* or *No* in the space at the left. Your answer will depend on the meaning of the italicized word. (Add 10 points for each correct answer.)

. . . . 1. Might a person be lonely in *isolation* from other people?

. . . . 2. Would you be likely to *chide* someone for doing you a favor?

. . . . 3. Is a blow from an ax likely to *sever* a clothesline?

. . . . 4. Is it *ethical* to take someone's bicycle without asking?

. . . . 5. Is it wise to drink a medicine that is for *external* use only?

. . . . 6. Would actors be glad if their performances received *ovations*?

. . . . 7. If you *comply* with an order, do you carry it out?

. . . . 8. Are *crags* likely to be found in a mountainous region?

. . . . 9. Must a coded message be *deciphered* before it can be understood?

. . . . 10. Could you get a *sumptuous* meal at a hot dog stand?

Spelling: Other Confusing Pairs

Many spelling errors are made with words that are similar in appearance and sound, though quite different in meaning.

The pairs of words below are often confused. By careful study of the appearance, sound, and meaning of these words, you can learn to avoid spelling mistakes when you write them. As you look at each word, pronounce it carefully and correctly. Try to memorize the word in the short sentence given to illustrate its meaning.

desert /déz ərt/	The camel is known as the "ship of the desert."
dessert /di zúrt/	Ice cream is my favorite dessert.
quiet /kwí ət/	Sunday afternoon was very quiet.
quite /kwīt/	Are you quite certain of your answer?
cloths /klauthz/	You will need two cloths for polishing the silver.
clothes /klōᵺz/	The whole family got new clothes for the holidays.
formally /fáur məl ē/	Louis was dressed too formally for a square dance.
formerly /fáur mər lē/	This is my cousin Doris, formerly of Nome, Alaska.
loose /lūs/	He has a loose tooth.
lose /lūz/	I will try not to lose my temper again.

Some pairs of words that cause spelling problems can be mastered if you learn to use a knowledge of both stress and word placement to help you decide between the confusing words. As you read the following examples, notice how stress and word placement give you clues to correct spelling.

to	I went to the post office to mail a package. (*To* is pronounced "tuh" and is unstressed. When the sound is "tuh," spell it *to*.)
too	There are too many demands on my time, too. (The vowel sound in *too* is pronounced like the vowel sound in *tool*. *Too* is always a stressed word in a sentence.)
all ready	We are all ready to begin the test. (*All* is slightly stressed; there is also a slight pause between *all* and *ready*. The sentence makes sense even when the two words are separated: We *all* are *ready* to begin the test.)
already	They have already left. (*Already* is said quickly, with no pause between *al* and *ready*. If the two parts of the word are separated, the sentence makes no sense: They *al* have *ready* left.)

all together	We were all together for the holidays.
altogether	Jeff was altogether wrong about that.
	(The same stress and word placement clues apply as with *all ready* and *already*.)

EXERCISE A Underline the words in the parentheses that make the sentences correct. (Add 10 points for each correct answer.)

1. What fun it was to be (all together, altogether) on New Year's Eve!

2. The prince bowed (formerly, formally) to the prime minister.

3. It is (all together, altogether) too cool to go swimming.

4. Many French people prefer fruit and cheese for (desert, dessert).

5. The rope on the anchor had come (loose, lose).

6. Alan is (quite, quiet) pleased with his new bicycle.

7. I am spending (too, to) much money on unimportant things.

8. We put on our old (clothes, cloths) and began to paint the bookcases.

9. It was (all ready, already) past midnight.

10. Your speech could use some improvement (to, too).

EXERCISE B In the blank in each sentence below, write the word from the pair in parentheses that correctly completes the sentence. (Add 20 points for each correct answer.)

1. Nights are very cool in the . . . . (dessert, desert)

2. Linda was . . . . to start the concert. (already, all ready)

3. Do you want . . . . go skiing this Saturday? (too, to)

4. This old sheet will make good dusting . . . . (clothes, cloths)

5. Are you . . . . certain you saw him? (all together, altogether)

REVIEW EXERCISE Be prepared to write the following words from dictation. Your teacher will read each word in a sentence. (Add 10 points for each correctly spelled word.)

| 1. compliment | 3. plain | 5. minor | 7. soul | 9. waist |
| 2. their | 4. fair | 6. peace | 8. borne | 10. who's |

FRAGMENTS AND RUN-ONS The paragraphs below contain sentence fragments and run-on sentences. Correct the sentence fragments by connecting them to the sentences with which they belong. (Draw a line through the incorrect capital letters and periods and add any necessary punctuation.) Correct the run-on sentences by making separate, complete sentences, adding periods and capital letters. (Add 5 points for each corrected fragment or run-on.)

1   Anne and some of her friends were interested in foreign sports cars,
2   they formed a club to study them. They enjoyed examining all of the
3   available information on the cars. Although they were too young to
4   drive. Each week one of the members reported on a car. At the
5   end of the month. They compared the cars that had been discussed.
6   One of the facts they immediately noticed was that all of the information
7   was given in metric units. Most of the members were familiar with the
8   metric system. They found it convenient to convert the metric units to
9   the English system. For the purpose of comparison with American cars.
10   The units of the metric system are the meter, the kilogram, and the
11   liter, the meter is used for length, the kilogram for mass, and the liter
12   for liquid volume. One meter is equal to 39.37 inches, one kilogram
13   to 2.2 pounds, and one liter to 1.06 quarts. The kilometer is a thousand
14   meters. Which is equal to 0.62 miles. Although it is easier to remember
15   that one meter is roughly forty inches, one kilometer slightly more than
16   half a mile, one kilogram about two pounds, and one liter a little more
17   than a quart. They wanted to obtain more accurate data than approxi-
18   mations would allow.
19   Anne was due to give her report that week, she was reporting on a
20   low-priced economy car made in Italy. The fuel tank held 28 liters. Anne
21   found that it held 29.7 quarts. By multiplying by 1.06. Since we buy fuel
22   by the gallon rather than by the quart. She divided this figure by 4. And
23   found that the tank held 7.42 gallons. This figure seemed very small to
24   Anne, she was used to cars that held about 20 gallons. She then checked

25   to see how far the car could travel. On one tankful of gas. The car would

26   get 35 miles to the gallon under ideal circumstances, by multiplying she

27   found that the car could go about 260 miles on one tank of gas. She also

28   discovered that the car was equipped with a fuel reserve indicator. A red

29   light that would show on the fuel gauge. When there were only four liters

30   of gas left in the tank. Anne converted this figure. And found that the

31   indicator lit when there were 1.1 gallons left. This meant that the car

32   could travel 38.5 miles. Before it ran out of fuel from the time that the

33   indicator first lit up.

34   Anne submitted her report to the group, they decided that the car

35   excelled in efficient use of fuel. They also liked its small size, it would be

36   an excellent choice for the city driver.

CAPITALIZATION Correct the capitalization errors in the sentences below: draw a line through any incorrect capital letters; cross out any incorrect small letter and write the capital letter above it. (Add 10 points for each correctly marked sentence.)

1. The Parthenon is an ancient greek temple built for the Goddess Athena.

2. Agatha Christie, whose most famous novel is *And then there were none,* wrote more than one hundred mysteries.

3. My Mother and father, aunt Claudine, and uncle Phil went to dinner at a new spanish restaurant.

4. The fourth of july fell on a monday that year.

5. The map shows that San francisco is about two hundred miles to the West of Los angeles.

6. The First National bank of Charleston, whose Chief Executive is president Frederick D. Greenleaf, is one of the oldest Banks in the southeast.

7. Antonia Fraser's masterful history, *mary, queen of scots,* contains as much adventure and excitement as several novels.

8. At summer school I took typing I, english, and Ancient history.

9. A display of Cosmetics at macy's drew many customers.

10. The death of queen Elizabeth I of England marked the end of the elizabethan Age.

PRONOUNS Underline the correct one of the two pronouns in the parentheses. (Add 10 points for each correct answer.)

1. (They, Them) and Gordon offered to clean out the garage for Dave and (we, us) if we would help them build their boat.

2. "It is Emilio and (I, me) you should have chosen," said Martha to the judges.

3. Trudy and (he, him) will represent our school at the regional spelling bee.

4. When I asked if Jeff was home, the voice said, "This is (he, him)."

5. Mom helped Cary and (I, me) to make a new transom for our boat.

6. (We, Us) had a slight accident on the river the other day.

7. My sister, who is a year younger, came with Charlotte and (I, me).

8. "It is for (we, us) girls to decide when we audition the other band and (they, them)," Esther explained.

SUBJECT AND VERB AGREEMENT Some of the sentences below have errors in agreement between subject and verb. If the sentence is correct, write *C* in the space at the right. If the sentence is incorrect, cross out the incorrect form of the verb and write the correct form in the space. (Add 10 points for each correctly marked sentence.)

1. Neither the Republican party nor the Democratic party have succeeded in balancing the budget.　　1. . . . .

2. A few of the members is unhappy about the increase in dues.　　2. . . . .

3. Either Peter or his brother are going to feed our dog while we are gone.　　3. . . . .

4. Everyone in our family have the habit of speaking out when something is the matter.　　4. . . . .

5. If somebody don't know us, it sounds as if we are fighting.　　5. . . . .

6. Actually, we are all still good friends, and nobody takes offense.　　6. . . . .

7. There's many people, however, who prefer anything to an argument.　　7. . . . .

8. Either of the two candidates are acceptable to the party.　　8. . . . .

9. Personally, I think brooding or sulking is a poor way
of working out one's problems.   9. . . . .

10. Why haven't each of the people waiting for the
announcement already been informed of the results? 10. . . . .

REGULAR AND IRREGULAR VERBS   If you find an incorrect verb form
in any of the following sentences, cross it out and write the correct form in the
space before the sentence. If the verb in any sentence is correct, write *C* in the
space before the sentence. (Add 5 points for each correct answer.)

. . . .   1. Bulldozers begun to demolish the house yesterday.

. . . .   2. I was afraid you had broke your arm.

. . . .   3. You should have drove more carefully.

. . . .   4. Nobody knew which road to take.

. . . .   5. The wagon was lying on its side.

. . . .   6. When you go to the library, please bring this book with you.

. . . .   7. She should have throwed him out at second base.

. . . .   8. He hasn't wrote home for three weeks.

. . . .   9. Someone must have spoken to her.

. . . .   10. Yesterday we swum across the lake.

. . . .   11. You might have chosen a stronger leader.

. . . .   12. Last evening we run into each other at the supermarket.

. . . .   13. Someone must have rode the horses too hard.

. . . .   14. You should have took your sister with you.

. . . .   15. This is the souvenir that Gretchen brung us from Germany.

. . . .   16. At three o'clock he lay down for a nap.

. . . .   17. Although I didn't like the taste, I drunk the medicine.

. . . .   18. They would have froze to death by morning.

. . . .   19. They wouldn't leave us go with them.

. . . .   20. Everyone must set as still as possible.

CHAPTER ELEVEN

Sentence Combining

This chapter of ENGLISH WORKSHOP will help you to write more mature, varied sentences. Sentence combining provides a valuable opportunity for you to work with sentence structure: to join closely related ideas, to show logical relationships, and to add variety, clarity, and rhythm to your writing.

LESSON 103

Combining with Adjectives and Adverbs

COMBINING WITH ADJECTIVES

While working on a composition, you might write down some ideas just as you think of them, without worrying about how they are related. When you read what you have written, you may find that closely related ideas appear in different sentences.

EXAMPLE   There is sand on Okracoke Island.
The sand is white.
The sand is fine.

These repetitious, short sentences can be combined.

There is fine, white sand on Okracoke Island.

In the example above, the three sentences have been combined by leaving out unnecessary words and placing the adjectives *white* and *fine* next to the word they modify.

An adjective is a word used to modify a noun or pronoun. In combining sentences with adjectives, place the adjectives as close as possible to the nouns and pronouns they modify.

EXAMPLE   I love the mountains.
The mountains are misty.
The mountains look purple.

I love the purple, misty mountains.

211

EXERCISE A   Combine each of the following groups of sentences by writing one complete sentence on the lines provided. Follow the examples on page 211. Be sure to add commas where necessary. You usually need commas to separate two or more adjectives that modify the same noun or pronoun. (Add 10 points for each correct sentence.)

1. The Himalayas are mountains in Asia.

   They are the tallest mountains in Asia. . . . .

   . . . .

2. You can see a view of Mount Everest from Darjeeling.

   It is a beautiful view.   . . . .

   . . . .

3. Tea bushes grow on the slopes of the hills near Darjeeling.

   The slopes are steep.

   The hills are fertile. . . . .

   . . . .

   . . . .

4. The Sherpas are people who live in Nepal.

   They are Tibetan people.

   They live in northeast Nepal. . . . .

   . . . .

   . . . .

5. The British trained the Sherpas to be climbers.

   The Sherpas were trained to be good climbers.

   The Sherpas are strong. . . . .

   . . . .

   . . . .

6. The danger in mountain climbing comes from the altitude and the cold.

   The greatest danger comes from these things.

   The altitude is high.

   The cold is bitter. . . . .

   . . . .

   . . . .

212

7. The sun reflecting on the snow can cause blindness.

   The sun is bright.

   The snow is white.

   The blindness is temporary. ....

   ....

8. The air at that altitude makes oxygen masks necessary.

   The air is thin.

   The altitude is high.

   The oxygen masks are expensive. ....

   ....

9. The cold can cause frostbite on fingers and toes.

   The cold is penetrating.

   The frostbite can be severe.

   The fingers and toes are exposed. ....

   ....

   ....

10. Climbers need boots and food for reaching altitudes.

    The boots must be light.

    They must also be durable.

    The food should be nutritious.

    The altitudes are high. ....

    ....

    ....

COMBINING WITH ADVERBS

An **adverb** is a word that modifies a verb, an adjective or another adverb.
You can combine sentences with adverbs much as you can with adjectives.

EXAMPLE Linda is learning to drive a car.
         She is learning <u>slowly</u>.

         <u>Slowly</u>, Linda is learning to drive a car. (combined sentence)
                                or
         Linda is learning <u>slowly</u> to drive a car.

Although an adjective needs to be as close as possible to the word it modifies, the writer can choose where to place the adverb, depending on the meaning desired.

Adverb placement can change emphasis too. When it comes at the beginning of the sentence, it seems more important.

EXAMPLE   Quietly, Teresa tiptoed down the hall.
Teresa tiptoed quietly down the hall.
Teresa tiptoed down the hall quietly.

When you combine sentences with adverbs, you must sometimes decide where in the sentence the adverbs will be most effective. Therefore, your answers for some of the sentences in the following exercise may not be exactly like those of your classmates.

EXERCISE B   Combine each of the following groups of sentences by writing one complete sentence on the lines provided. (Add 20 points for each correct answer.)

1. Robert put the game away.

   He did this quickly. . . . .

   . . . .

2. The eighth grade will learn the wisdom of silence.

   They will do this eventually. . . . .

   . . . .

3. The Lees won the sweepstakes and became rich.

   They became extremely rich. . . . .

   . . . .

4. Sharon had heard her family speak of General Washington.

   They spoke reverently of General Washington.

   She heard them often. . . . .

   . . . .

   . . . .

5. The musicians set up the instruments.

   They did this quietly.

   They did this first. . . . .

   . . . .

   . . . .

Combining with Adjective and Adverb Phrases

A **prepositional phrase** is a group of words which begins with a preposition and ends with a noun or pronoun. A prepositional phrase modifying a noun or pronoun is called an **adjective phrase**; a prepositional phrase modifying a verb, adjective, or adverb is called an **adverb phrase**. Combining with adjective and adverb prepositional phrases is very much like combining with single-word adjectives and adverbs.

Just as adjectives must be placed as close as possible to the nouns and pronouns they modify, so adjective phrases must also be close to the words they modify. An adjective phrase often follows the word it describes.

> EXAMPLE   Alexander the Great conquered many lands.
> These lands were in the Middle east.
>
> Alexander the Great conquered many lands <u>in the Middle East</u>.   (combined sentence)

On the other hand, adverb phrases, just like adverbs, can sometimes be placed where you, the writer, think they will be most effective.

> EXAMPLE   Alexander's army refused, <u>at the Indus River</u>, to go farther.
>
> Alexander's army refused to go farther <u>at the Indus River</u>.
>
> <u>At the Indus River</u>, Alexander's army refused to go farther.
> (The last sentence is the smoothest.)

EXERCISE A   Combine each group of sentences by writing one sentence on the lines provided. Use prepositional phrases to combine the sentences. (Add 10 points for each correct sentence.)

1. Alexander the Great's father was the king.

   He was the king of Macedonia.   ....

   ....

2. When Alexander was young, he saw some wild horses.

   The horses were in the marketplace.   ....

   ....

3. One horse threw any rider.

   It was a horse with a deep black coat.   ....

   ....

215

4. Alexander's father, Philip, wanted to destroy the black horse.

It was the horse with the mean temper. ....

....

5. Alexander looked at the shadow.

The shadow was in front of the horse. ....

....

6. The horse's shadow moved as the horse jumped.

The shadow moved on the ground. ....

....

7. Alexander recognized the horse's fear.

It was the fear of its own shadow. ....

....

8. He grabbed the reins and turned the animal around.

The reins were on the horse. ....

....

9. The horse no longer saw the frightening shadow.

The shadow was of itself.

The shadow was on the ground. ....

....

....

10. The story is an example.

It is an example of Alexander the Great's intelligence.

It is an example of Alexander the Great's compassion. ....

....

....

Combining Subjects, Verbs, and Independent Clauses

COMPOUND SUBJECTS AND COMPOUND VERBS

When two (or more) connected subjects in a sentence have the same verb, the two (or more) of them together are called a **compound subject**. Similarly, when two or more connected verbs in a sentence have the same subject, the two or more of them together are called a **compound verb**. It is often good writing practice to combine closely related sentences so that the combined sentence has a compound subject or a compound verb.

EXAMPLES The cat will have to stay outside.
The dog will have to stay outside.

The cat <u>and</u> the dog will have to stay outside. (combined sentence with compound subject)

José will replace the broken window.
He will fix the window shade.

José will replace the broken window <u>and</u> fix the window shade. (combined sentence with compound verb)

The conjunctions used to connect the parts of a compound subject are *and, or, both—and, either—or, neither—nor*. The choice of the conjunction depends upon the meaning of the sentence. The conjunctions used to connect compound verbs are the same as for compound subjects, except that the conjunction *but* may also be used.

A sentence may sometimes contain both a compound subject and a compound verb.

EXERCISE A Combine the groups of sentences so that the combined sentence has a compound subject, a compound verb, or both a compound subject and a compound verb. Be sure the subject and the verb agree in number. (Add 10 points for each correct sentence.)

A. Marcy wants to go camping during summer vacation.

 Her friend Naomi wants to go camping during summer vacation. ...
 Marcy and her friend Naomi want to go camping during summer vacation.

1. They will hike in Rocky Mountain National Park.

 They will pitch their tents in Hidden Valley. ....

2. Last year Marcy walked up Trail Ridge to the alpine meadows.
   She went fishing in the Fall River. . . . .
   . . . .
   . . . .

3. Naomi is interested in watching for bighorn sheep.
   Marcy is interested in watching for bighorn sheep. . . . .
   . . . .
   . . . .

4. Sheep usually graze on the high slopes.
   They also wander down near Sheep Lake. . . . .
   . . . .
   . . . .

5. Marcy has plenty of equipment for camping.
   Naomi has plenty of camping equipment. . . . .
   . . . .
   . . . .

6. The pair will bring freeze-dried food.
   They will catch fish in the brooks and lakes. . . . .
   . . . .
   . . . .

7. Marcy has not been camping without an adult before.
   Neither has Naomi. . . . .
   . . . .

8. Naomi's father will drive out for the weekend.
   He will take them hiking above the timberline. . . . .
   . . . .
   . . . .

9. Marcy is looking forward to the trip.
   Naomi is looking forward to the trip.
   Both are excited about camping in the mountains. . . . .
   . . . .
   . . . .

10. Camping is among the girls' favorite pastimes.

Hiking is among the girls' favorite pastimes.

....

....

COMPOUND SENTENCES

Two short, related sentences can often join to form a compound sentence. A compound sentence contains two or more simple sentences, usually connected by the conjunction *and, but, or,* or *nor.*

> EXAMPLE Ben Franklin wanted to be a sailor. (simple sentence)
> His father decided he would be a printer's apprentice. (simple sentence)
> Ben Franklin wanted to be a sailor, but his father decided he would be a printer's apprentice. (compound sentence)

The choice of the conjunction *and, but, or,* or *nor,* depends upon the meaning of the sentence. In the example above, there is a contrast between what Ben Franklin wanted and what his father wanted. Therefore *but* is the best conjunction to choose.

Combining short sentences into compound sentences will show the close relationship between the ideas in the short sentences. If two short sentences are unrelated, however, or unequal in importance, it is best to keep these sentences apart.

> EXAMPLES The neighbors bought a new volleyball net.
> I bruised my knee in the game last night. (These ideas are not closely related; therefore, they should not be joined into a compound sentence.)
>
> The Drama Circle is staging *The Tempest* this month.
> I didn't go. (These ideas are not equal in importance; therefore they should not be joined into a compound sentence.)

EXERCISE B Most of the following items consist of two or more closely related sentences. Combine these sentences into a single compound sentence using the conjunctions *and, but, or,* or *nor.* (Reminder: Always use a comma before a conjunction when it joins the parts of a compound sentence.) A few items consist of unrelated or unequal sentences. Do not combine these sentences. Write U on the lines provided. (Add 10 points for each correct answer.)

1. Ben Franklin was an apprentice printer for his brother James.

He did not like working for him. ....

....

....

2. Ben read many books after work.

   In his writing, he tried to copy the authors' styles. . . . .

   . . . .

   . . . .

3. Ben and his brother printed the newspaper.

   Ben also had to sell the paper on the street. . . . .

   . . . .

   . . . .

4. The paper sold well.

   The paper attacked the Massachusetts Assembly. . . . .

   . . . .

5. Ben decided to run away from his brother.

   Ships were a major means of transportation in those days. . . . .

   . . . .

   . . . .

6. He first went to New York.

   There was no work for printers in that city. . . . .

   . . . .

7. He took a ferry to Perth Amboy.

   A storm drove the ferry onto the rocks. . . . .

   . . . .

   . . . .

8. He walked most of the way to Philadelphia.

   This city was bigger than New York or Boston. . . . .

   . . . .

   . . . .

9. Franklin finally started his own print shop.

   It became successful very quickly. . . . .

   . . . .

10. Ben Franklin started *Poor Richard's Almanac.*

    This publication made him famous. . . . .

    . . . .

Combining with Adjective Clauses

Sometimes two closely related sentences can be combined by turning one of the sentences into an adjective clause.

EXAMPLE We had homework on Halloween.
It fell on a school night this year.

We had homework on Halloween, which fell on a school night this year. (combined sentence with adjective clause)

An **adjective clause** is a subordinate clause which is used as an adjective to modify a noun or a pronoun. Adjective clauses are introduced with a relative pronoun: *who, whom, whose, which,* or *that.*

EXAMPLES Mr. Bry is the man who bought my dog. (modifies noun)
My dog is the one that has long ears. (modifies pronoun)

When writing adjective clauses, choose the correct relative pronoun. Study the examples below.

EXAMPLES (who) Her sister is the doctor who won the award. (*Who* refers to people. It is used as the subject of the clause.)

(whom) Tracy Austin, whom I have seen in person, won the U.S. Open. (*Whom* refers to people and is used as the object in the clause.)

When joining sentences with an adjective clause, be sure to put the adjective clause next to the noun or pronoun it modifies.

EXERCISE Each pair of sentences can be combined by making the italicized sentence into an adjective clause. Write the sentence on the lines provided. Be sure the clause comes right after the word it modifies. The first one is done for you. (Add 10 points for each correct sentence.)

A. Yellowstone Park is famous for its geysers and bubbling caldrons.

It is bigger than the state of Delaware. *Yellowstone Park, which is bigger than the state of Delaware, is famous for its geysers and bubbling caldrons.*

1. The newest park is called Gates of the Arctic.

It is four times the size of Yellowstone Park. ....

....

....

221

2. Many national parks are too crowded with visitors.

   These visitors threaten the natural environment. ....

   ....

   ....

3. One national park in Hawaii contains active volcanoes.

   They sometimes spew fire and lava. ....

   ....

4. Forest rangers work deep within the national forest.

   Most people never see the rangers. ....

   ....

5. At Mesa Verde you can climb down into kivas.

   They were built by ancient cliff dwellers. ....

   ....

   ....

6. My Aunt Laura guides rafts down the Colorado River.

   Her job is filled with danger. ....

   ....

7. In Virginia there is a monument to Booker T. Washington.

   He made many contributions to education. ....

   ....

   ....

8. Dinosaur National Monument is in Colorado.

   This monument interests me the most. ....

   ....

   ....

9. Terry will enjoy Acadia National Park.

   Terry loves to camp by the sea. ....

   ....

10. Rangers scan the horizon for forest fires.

    They live in tall watchtowers. ....

    ....

Combining with Adjective Clauses for Emphasis

When you combine two sentences by turning one of the sentences into an adjective clause, you may face a choice: Which sentence should become the adjective clause and which sentence should remain an independent clause? The choice usually depends on which idea you, the writer, consider more important and therefore wish to emphasize.

The more important idea will receive greater emphasis in the independent clause.

EXAMPLE   Muhammad Ali is the first boxer to regain the heavyweight crown twice.
He is a popular sports figure around the world.

Muhammad Ali, who is the first boxer to regain the heavyweight crown twice, is a popular sports figure around the world. (This version emphasizes Ali's popularity.)
or
Muhammad Ali, who is a popular sports figure around the world, is the first boxer to regain the heavyweight crown twice. (This version emphasizes Ali's regaining the heavyweight crown twice.)

Often the context of your writing will determine which ideas should be emphasized. If the sentences above, for example, were part of a paragraph about Ali's heavyweight fights, then the second version would be a better choice than the first.

EXERCISE   Rewrite the following pairs of sentences by turning one of the sentences into an adjective clause. For the first five pairs, emphasize the idea of the first sentence. For the second five pairs, emphasize the idea of the second sentence. (Add 10 points for each correct sentence.)

A. Humpback whales are known for their unearthly songs.
These whales winter in the tropics. *Humpback whales, which winter in the tropics, are known for their unearthly songs.*

(This version emphasizes the idea of the first sentence by placing it in the independent clause.)

1. Whales are endangered in many parts of the world.
Whales have been killed for their oil. ....

....

....

2. A humpback whale will not attack a person.
   This whale has a very gentle nature. . . . .

   . . . .

3. Roger Payne wrote an article in this month's magazine.
   He is an expert on whale sounds and songs. . . . .

   . . . .

4. Whales must often come to the water's surface.
   Whales breathe air like other mammals. . . . .

   . . . .

5. Whales usually inspect but do not harm divers.
   The divers are exploring beneath the water. . . . .

   . . . .

6. Whales possess enormous strength.
   Whales sometimes flip completely out of the water. . . . .

   . . . .

7. Baleen whales live on tiny shrimp called krill.
   Baleen whales are huge. . . . .

   . . . .

8. Whales can communicate with one another.
   Whales are obviously intelligent creatures. . . . .

   . . . .

   . . . .

9. The blue whale is the largest creature on earth.
   At the Natural History Museum we saw a picture of the blue whale.

   . . . .

   . . . .

10. Humpback whales spend breeding season in Hawaii or Bermuda.
    Humpback whales sing as they swim. . . . .

    . . . .

Combining with Adverb Clauses

You can improve two choppy, related sentences by turning one sentence into an adverb clause.

An **adverb clause** is a subordinate clause used as an adverb. It may tell *how, when, where, why, to what extent,* or *under what condition* something is done.

EXAMPLE   We waited <u>until the last show began.</u> (adverb clause showing *when*)

An adverb clause begins with a **subordinating conjunction**.

SOME COMMON SUBORDINATING CONJUNCTIONS

as if, as though (show *how*)
after, as, before, since, until, when, while (show *when*)
where, wherever (show *where*)
because, since, so that (show *why*)
than, as long as (show *to what extent*)
although, if, unless (show *under what condition*)

To combine two sentences by using an adverb clause, choose the subordinating conjunction that shows the exact relationship between the two sentences.

EXAMPLE   Daniel Boone climbed the tree.
The bear was chasing him.

Daniel Boone climbed the tree <u>because the bear was chasing him.</u>

Adverb clauses can also be placed at the beginning of sentences.

EXAMPLE   <u>Because the bear was chasing him,</u> Daniel Boone climbed the tree. (Note: An adverb clause at the beginning of a sentence must be followed by a comma.)

EXERCISE   Combine each pair of sentences by writing one complete sentence with an adverb clause. Choose one of the subordinating conjunctions in parentheses to introduce the adverb clause. Add commas where they are necessary. (Add 10 points for each correct answer.)

1. Many people want to be ballet dancers.

   Ballet dancing seems to be a glamorous profession. (*after, because*)

   . . . .

   . . . .

225

2. The United States Constitution will last another two hundred years.
   We maintain our love for freedom. (*although, if*) ·················

   ···

   ···

3. We sat through movie matinees every Saturday.
   We were seven or eight years old. (*so that, when*) ·················

   ···

   ···

4. An athlete has no chance to enter the Olympic Games.
   He or she begins training very early. (*unless, so that*) ·············

   ···

   ···

5. Preston must watch what he eats. ·······························

   He won't become too heavy. (*so that, as if*) ·····················

   ···

6. There is trouble.
   There are hungry bears and unguarded campsites. (wherever, unless)

   ···

   ···

7. We will do all our shopping in this store.
   The prices seem steep. (*although, unless*) ·······················

   ···

8. Melinda is not eligible to run again.
   She won the election last year. (*as though, since*) ·················

   ···

9. The pitcher threw warm-up tosses.
   The batter took some practice swings. (*while, wherever*) ···········

   ···

10. Marsha already had received her prize in the mail.
    Phil collected all thirty-three box tops. (*if, before*) ·················

    ···

    ···

Combining with More Than One Clause

Often you can combine three short, choppy sentences into one sentence by using clauses.

EXAMPLE   Armando is a great soccer fan.
Jack prefers basketball.
He learned it from his brother

Armando is a great soccer fan, but Jack prefers basketball, which he learned from his brother.

The first two sentences are rewritten as two independent clauses joined by the conjunction *but*. The third sentence is rewritten as an adjective clause modifying *basketball*. It is introduced by the relative pronoun *which*.

Always choose the type of clause that expresses the exact relationship between the sentences.

EXERCISE Combine each group of sentences into one smooth, clear sentence by using independent and subordinate clauses. Begin each clause with the word given in parentheses. Check your sentences to be sure the punctuation is correct. The first one is done for you. (Add 10 points for each correct sentence.)

A. Carmen Juarez lives in Los Angeles.

Her parents own an attractive shop. (where)

It sells handmade crafts. (that) *Carmen Juarez lives in Los Angeles, where her parents own an attractive shop that sells handmade crafts.*

1. Los Angeles was settled by Spanish explorers.

They first arrived there in 1769. (who)

The city has had a strong Spanish heritage ever since. (and) . . . .

. . . .

. . . .

. . . .

2. Carmen speaks Spanish at home.

Her parents are more comfortable with that language. (because)

She also speaks English fluently. (but) . . . .

. . . .

. . . .

    227

3. Carmen wants to become a teacher.
   She can teach Hispanic children. (so that) ....
   ....

4. Carmen works both at school and in her family's store.
   She still has time to play the guitar. (but) ....
   ....

5. The Juarezes are fond of Mexican cooking.
   It is a mixture of Aztec, Mayan, and Spanish dishes. (which)
   They serve it at gourmet feasts. (and) ....
   ....

   ....

6. A different environment surrounds Mary Pinkney.
   Her home is in Vermont. (whose) ....
   ....

7. Mary's ancestors were immigrants.
   They came from England seeking religious freedom. (who)
   England recognized only one religion. (because) ....
   ....

   ....

8. Mary is studying Spanish in school.
   She would like to visit Mexico. (because) ....
   ....

9. Mary would like to earn money.
   She can work only in the afternoons. (but)
   Jobs are scarce. (and) ....
   ....

   ....

10. Mrs. Leavitt suggested that she raise chickens.
    She is a 4-H advisor. (who)
    The chickens are easy to care for. (which) ....
    ....

    ....

Review of Sentence Combining

Here are two paragraphs to help you review what you have learned. Each tells a story, but the sentences are short and choppy and do not show the relationships of the ideas in each paragraph.

EXERCISE   Rewrite each paragraph below, combining sentences in all the ways you have learned in this chapter. You will need to leave out repetitious words and to do some rearranging in order to make the paragraph read more smoothly. Make all the changes you think necessary, but do not change the meaning of the paragraph. Add correct punctuation.

HURRICANES

A.   Hurricanes are tropical storms. The storms are powerful. Hurricanes begin over water. It is ocean water. The water is warm. The water is near the equator. A hurricane produces energy. A hurricane produces as much energy as several thousand atomic bombs. A hurricane produces this much in a second. The energy is spread over an area. The area is several hundred miles. Winds in a hurricane blow more than 75 miles per hour. These winds sometimes reach 120 miles per hour. Hurricanes move over land. They cause great devastation. The devastation is because of their winds. Now meteorologists track hurricanes. They track them accurately. The meteorologists can predict their path. People can be evacuated.

. . . .

. . . .

. . . .

. . . .

. . . .

. . . .

. . . .

. . . .

. . . .

. . . .

. . . .

. . . .

B. Emily Dickinson lived during the nineteenth century. She has become an interesting subject for biographers. She wrote a great deal of poetry. She wrote chiefly for herself. She sometimes wrote for a few friends. She wrote many of her poems on scraps of paper. They were beautiful poems. She hid the scraps of paper in a drawer. She studied at Mount Holyoke Female Seminary. It is in Massachusetts. She studied there for a short while. Then she became a recluse. She seldom left her house. She wore white dresses. She wore them always. No one knows exactly why.

....

....

....

....

....

....

....

....

....

....

....

....

CHAPTER TWELVE

Writing Effective Paragraphs

The first eleven chapters of our ENGLISH WORKSHOP have all been concerned, in one way or another, with writing effective sentences. By now, we know what it takes to make a proper sentence—not a fragment or run-on—and how to assemble the parts of a sentence so that they will make good sense.

Well-constructed sentences are the building blocks of all good writing. We organize our thoughts into words, our words into sentences, our sentences into still larger units. These larger units—paragraphs—are as important to good writing as the sentences of which they are composed. In this chapter, we shall see how strong paragraphs are built up and how the paragraphs themselves are fitted together into longer compositions.

LESSON 111

Organizing Effective Paragraphs

The main reason for dividing writing into paragraphs is to enable the reader to follow our ideas easily. A good paragraph deals with only one topic. When it ends and another paragraph begins, readers know that the writer is going to present another topic or a different part of the same topic.

A paragraph is a series of sentences developing one topic.

EXAMPLE   **I still vividly remember the position of every rock, bush, and tree in my old hideaway.** It's nearly seven years now since I hid behind the big rock at the entrance to the unused lot that was our playground and battlefield. My friends and I played *hide-and-go-seek* and *cops and robbers.* Sometimes we chased each other in and out of the thick, tall yew bushes that grew along one side of the lot. If we became tired of playing, we picked nuts from the hazelnut tree at the back of the lot. I think I'll always remember every detail of that place.

The preceding paragraph is about one thing, the hideaway. Notice how the writer starts out with a sentence that tells us what the paragraph is going to be about.

The next paragraph is an example of poor organization and poor focus. Instead of having a single topic, it has several. We are never sure what the paragraph is about.

EXAMPLE   My cat seems to get more fleas in the summertime than in the winter. My cat's name is Toby-O and she doesn't like the snow. She lifts up her feet as if she were walking along in glue. Fleas don't bother her, though. Maybe it is because the snow kills the fleas. We can't tell. But Toby-O does a lot of scratching in August. That's when we go on vacation. Some people like to go on vacation in winter. I'm not sure that Toby-O would like that.

This paragraph has no specific subject. Is the paragraph about fleas, or whether Toby-O likes summer better than winter, or whether vacations are better in the summer or winter? There are simply too many subjects for one paragraph.

One way of correcting this paragraph is to turn it into two (or more) paragraphs. That way, each paragraph has just one topic.

EXERCISE   Each of these paragraphs has more than one topic. Decide which is the best subject for each paragraph and underline the sentences that do not belong in the paragraph. The sentences that are not underlined ought to make a good, coherent paragraph.

1. Once in late August, a noisy mockingbird kept me awake all night. It seemed to be living in the tree branches right outside my window, so that its chirping was as loud as if it were in the room. At first I knocked on the window, but the bird would not be quiet. People are like that sometimes, too. Then I went outside. Sometimes you wonder about why some people are noisy when you don't want them to be. The mockingbird really seemed to be mocking me. It seemed to chirp louder when I came out with the flashlight. I shined it directly on the bird, but the bird kept chirping. Finally, I had to shake the tree hard before it flew off. Now I know why they call them mockingbirds.

2. We went canoeing when I attended camp last year. Most of the trees there are pine, but some are ash, and others are oak. The canoe trip took us to a large lake named Bear Pond. Calling it a pond was some kind of joke, because it took us two and a half hours to canoe around it. We had a campsite on the far side of the lake. The canoes were hauled up on the little beach there, and we cooked dinner over an open fire. On the next day, we returned to camp, tired but happy. I liked all the trees, too, but we didn't have enough time to do much exploring in the woods.

The Topic Sentence

The topic of a paragraph should be stated in a single sentence somewhere in the paragraph. This sentence is called the topic sentence.

The topic sentence is often the first sentence in the paragraph. Since the readers know what to look for, they can grasp the other ideas in the paragraph more easily when the topic sentence comes first.

EXAMPLE   **Volcanoes strike with alarming surprise and do a great deal of damage if they strike a city.** The Roman resort town of Pompeii, Italy, was totally destroyed when Mount Vesuvius erupted in A.D. 79. The volcano poured its lava out so suddenly that people did not have time to leave their homes. Travelers were struck down in the streets. Excavations have shown that shops still had their wares on display. The entire city was covered with almost twenty feet of lava, and every citizen was killed. Other towns and cities have shared the same fate as Pompeii, although none were covered so quickly, and none were so totally destroyed.

When we want to build up suspense or summarize a number of points, it is often a good idea to put the topic sentence at the end of the paragraph. See how the position of the topic sentence affects this paragraph:

EXAMPLE   At first it was just dark and hot and humid, with no breath of air stirring. A few merchants on Main Street nailed battens over their plate-glass windows. Small pleasure boats on trailers trundled up the road from the yacht basin. The ominous red and black flag hung limp over the Coast Guard station. Then the breeze began to blow, fitfully at first, but relentlessly harder. It began to rain, softly at first, then with increasing insistence. A sudden hard gust banged a shutter somewhere. The loudspeaker over the door of the music shop still blared deafeningly, but there was nobody to listen. The streets were deserted except for an occasional police car cruising slowly, its windshield wipers rocking madly against the deluge. **A hurricane was coming.**

EXERCISE A   Underline the topic sentence in each of the following paragraphs.

1. I never grow tired of making airplane models. I like to watch each model take shape. As soon as one is completed I try to fly it. Sometimes I attempt to fly it when the weather is not good, and my plane is wrecked. Then off I go to build another one!

2. A little after six o'clock, the first light began to show in the east. Thin, dark clouds hung over the sunrise, turning a faint pink in the rising light. Gradually the light filled the sky until the last clouds were gone and the sun hung bright and clear above the trees. It was going to be another cloudless, beautiful day.

EXERCISE B The following short paragraphs do not have topic sentences. Circle the sentence provided below each paragraph that you think would make a good topic sentence. Write *B* or *E* after your sentence to show whether you think it belongs at the beginning or the end of the paragraph.

1. There aren't very many people who dance. At the last party there were lots of people sitting around the wall. A games party could be organized so that there would be fun for everybody. We could set up Ping-Pong, card tables, and, just in case, a phonograph and a space in the corner for those who do want to dance.

A. One thing we want to do is to make sure there are plenty of games for people.

B. We can have some dancing, but we must be sure there are games for people.

C. If we want to, we can set up a Ping-Pong tournament for the party.

2. It was a sprawling, comfortable-looking old-fashioned house, with an enormous screened porch that faced the water. The yard, which the real-estate agent said was an acre, was filled with big old trees of every description, and I could hear birds twittering in the dappled shade. In the rear of the property was an old stable. My sister's eyes twinkled when she glanced at it. "I could have my woodworking shop out there," she said.

A. The first house we went to look at in our new town delighted us.

B. The day was one of those beautiful, calm summer delights.

C. Fortunately, the real-estate agent was easy to talk to, and he seemed to like us.

Writing the Topic Sentence

Not every sentence is useful as a topic sentence. Some sentences are much too broad and try to cover too large a subject. The best topic sentence has a single, clear subject that is just right for development.

The topic sentence has a clearly limited subject and makes a clear statement about that subject.

Your topic sentence will be good if you follow these suggestions:
1. Choose a single specific subject.
2. Make a clear statement about that subject.
3. Be sure you can develop the subject with facts, reasons, or examples.

Examine the following examples. Note that the topic sentences that are too broad are not very interesting. They lead the reader to respond with, "So what?" There is no specific reason to read on. This is not so, however, with the revised sentences, which take the same subject and make it more specific.

EXAMPLES   Too broad: Treats are fun after a game.
               Specific: A double-dip chocolate ice-cream cone after a rough ball game is my idea of fun.

               Too broad: Boating is dangerous.
               Specific: On Bear Pond I had an accident so frightening that I realized just how dangerous boating can be.

               Too broad: Some fellows got lost in the woods.
               Specific: Three students from the Buchanan School seventh grade were lost for a whole afternoon when they went searching through the woods for buried pirate treasure.

All the specific sentences give a specific time and a specific place, and define general terms such as *treats* with exact references such as *double-dip chocolate ice-cream cone*. This kind of exactness makes each second sentence more interesting and useful than the first.

EXERCISE A   In the spaces before each of the following topic sentences, write either *Too broad* or *Specific*.

.... 1. I would really love to fly.

.... 2. My mother wants me to study piano so that I can understand music better.

.... 3. Some countries do not want all their young people to go to school.

.... 4. I think school is very important.

.... 5. Dr. Jones took one look at my brother Larry and called an ambulance.

.... 6. Most people enjoy movies.

.... 7. Some people like books.

.... 8. When I read *My Friend, Flicka*, everybody in our house had to walk around on tiptoe.

.... 9. Many towns have a problem with garbage.

.... 10. Hiking is the most popular activity in Lakota Park.

EXERCISE B Write a specific topic sentence based on the following lists of ideas. Write it in the space provided.

Topic sentence: ....

....

List of ideas: A. I lived in a community where there were snowstorms.
             B. The snow tied up traffic and closed schools.

Topic sentence: ....

....

List of ideas: A. I like to read stories about history.
             B. My favorite period is the American Civil War.
             C. I especially enjoy reading about the great Civil War generals, Ulysses S. Grant and Robert E. Lee.

Topic sentence: ....

....

List of ideas: A. Once a year we go up to the lake for a week.
             B. My brother, Jimmy, and I go fishing.
             C. The lake is stocked with pike and bass.

Developing an Idea in a Paragraph

The topic sentence of a paragraph states the main idea of the paragraph. The rest of the sentences in a paragraph support the topic sentence by adding specific information.

Develop a paragraph by adding details that support the topic sentence of the paragraph.

EXAMPLE (1) It is interesting for a person who is used to living in hilly country to drive through a part of the United States which seems absolutely flat. (2) Central Illinois has very few hills and it is easy to see objects many miles away. (3) When we drove through this area, we noticed that a grain elevator on the horizon seemed to recede as we approached it. (4) I kept thinking there was something wrong with the speedometer on our car. (5) On the hilly roads at home, we never see anything until we are nearly there. (6) I enjoyed the wide, open feeling of the plains.

Analyze the construction of the paragraph above. It starts with a topic sentence (sentence 1). It adds a few facts (sentence 2). Then comes an impression, followed by a very brief incident (sentences 3, 4, and 5). It concludes with a summarizing sentence which ties in with the topic sentence (sentence 6).

Develop a paragraph by adding examples that support the topic sentence of the paragraph.

The following paragraph uses examples for its development. It starts with a topic sentence and then presents specific examples to back up the topic sentence.

EXAMPLE (1) Birthdays in our family are special because they seem to fall on special days. My dad's birthday comes on the first day of spring, and he likes to celebrate it by planting his garden. My mom's birthday is on the Fourth of July. We pretend all the parades and fireworks are for her. My sister, Jewel, has her birthday on the day after Halloween when there is always plenty of candy in the house. My birthday is best of all because it is right in the middle of the holiday season in December.

The first sentence sets up the opportunity to use each family member's birthday as an example. Each of the following sentences gives us a specific example, or fact, about each birthday.

237

Develop a paragraph by adding reasons that support the topic sentence.

The following paragraph uses reasons to support and develop the topic sentence. Note that the topic sentence has a single, clear subject for development.

EXAMPLE **Our school should plant a vegetable garden in the old lot behind the garage.** The land there is now an eyesore littered with bottles, cans, and other debris; a garden would improve our school's appearance. Vegetable gardening would also give many students the chance to learn about soil, minerals, and vegetation. These lessons could surely enhance science instruction. Furthermore, fresh fruits and vegetables grown in our very own garden would make our cafeteria menu more appetizing.

This paragraph gives three reasons why a vegetable garden should be planted. Each reason supports the topic sentence.

Many paragraphs you read in books and magazines develop topic sentences with both reasons and examples or a combination of reasons, examples, and other supporting details. Mixing details in a single paragraph can work only if every sentence adds to, supports, or otherwise develops the topic sentence.

EXERCISE A The topic sentence and a summing-up sentence are provided for a paragraph. In the spaces following, add two or three sentences of your own that add useful details and make a good paragraph.

1. The flashing UFO streaked across the midnight sky. . . . .

. . . .

. . . .

. . . .

. . . .

. . . .

. . . .

I stood looking at this amazing spectacle and wondered if anyone would ever believe what I saw.

EXERCISE B Each topic sentence is followed by a short list of examples. Use each topic sentence (or reword it) to write a single paragraph developed by examples. You may use the examples given or provide your own.

1. TOPIC SENTENCE   I enjoy having lots of unusual pets.
    EXAMPLES   A. Silly-Dilly, my box turtle

B. Mosso, the pet gerbil
C. Toots, my swordtail tropical fish
D. Lester, the de-scented skunk

YOUR PARAGRAPH

. . . .

. . . .

. . . .

. . . .

. . . .

. . . .

. . . .

2. TOPIC SENTENCE Energy conservation begins at home.
   EXAMPLES   1. Shutting off lights not in use
                  2. Putting insulation around windows
                  3. Using appliances wisely

YOUR PARAGRAPH

. . . .

. . . .

. . . .

. . . .

. . . .

. . . .

. . . .

EXERCISE C   Two lists follow. The first is a list of topics that can be developed by using details. The second list is of topics that can be developed by using specific examples. Your job is to take one topic from either list and write a good hundred-word paragraph.

1. Topics to develop by details:
   A. What happened in the recent adventure book you read
   B. Visiting a grandparent
   C. Getting ready for a trip
   D. My neighborhood
   E. How I get to school
2. Topics to develop by specific examples:
   A. The four most exciting days of the year
   B. The baseball teams I like and those I dislike

C. Things I most like to do
D. Animals I'd most like to be like
E. How to make money after school

YOUR PARAGRAPH

. . . .

. . . .

. . . .

. . . .

. . . .

. . . .

. . . .

. . . .

EXERCISE D Choose a subject from the following list and develop your paragraph by using reasons. Remember that a reason explains or defends your topic sentence.

1. Every family needs a pet dog (cat, gerbil, etc.).
2. People should be friendly to someone who has just moved into their neighborhood.
3. I had to play unusually well in my most memorable baseball game (soccer game, football game, field-hockey game, etc.).
4. Studying history is easier if you are interested in it to begin with.
5. Playing with fireworks can be dangerous.

YOUR PARAGRAPH

. . . .

. . . .

. . . .

. . . .

. . . .

. . . .

. . . .

. . . .

. . . .

Organizing Coherent Paragraphs

It is always best to plan a paragraph before you write it. An outline will help you decide what points to cover in your paragraph.

List the main idea and the supporting ideas in the form of an outline.

Begin your outline with a topic sentence. Then make a list of the supporting ideas that will develop this sentence. Discard those that are not related to the main idea of the paragraph.

EXAMPLE   Topic sentence   I'll never take my little brother to a horror movie again.

           Supporting ideas A. He couldn't sit still.
           (reasons)   B. He spilled soda all over my pants.
                           C. He shook the theater with his screams.
                           D. After the movie was over, he said, "What was so scary about that?"

Arrange the sentences in a paragraph in a sensible order.

The order in which supporting ideas are presented often makes the difference between a mediocre paragraph and a good one.

If you are relating an incident—telling about a series of events—*time order* is usually the best method to use. Establish the order in which events happened, usually beginning with the first occurrence.

A paragraph may be organized by the *order of importance* of ideas, especially if you are presenting a conclusion. You may begin with the least important idea and build up to the most important one.

If you are describing a scene, then *space order* may be the best way to organize your paragraph. You may wish to describe objects nearby, then those farther back, and finally the objects in the background.

In the three paragraphs that follow, sentences are arranged by three different methods—time order, order of importance, and space order. No one method is necessarily better than another. The one you choose will usually depend on what you are writing about.

Time
Order   When we first moved to New York City from Puerto Rico, I had trouble adjusting to my new surroundings. For about a month we stayed with my aunt and uncle. Although they were very nice to me, I felt like a visitor in an unfamiliar house. It was strange to be living with so many people. After we got our own apartment, I felt more comfortable. We could unpack all the little things that add warmth to a home. I began to make more friends because I felt

                                                               241

more at ease inviting them to my house. Now that we have been here for two years, I can truly say that I really enjoy living in New York.

Order of
Importance
Edward Weston, America's most durable walker, has completed some amazing journeys on foot. In 1861, to win a bet, Weston walked from Boston, Massachusetts, to Washington, D. C., in only ten days. In 1879, Weston captured the world championship of walking by traveling 550 miles in a mere six days. Weston's greatest feat, however, came in 1907. In that year, Weston made it from Portland, Maine, to Chicago, Illinois (1,237 miles), in under twenty-five days. He was sixty-eight years old at the time.

Space
Order
Now that autumn is past and leaves no longer block the view, I can see the red-brick tower of the school from my bedroom window. If I look in the other direction, I can see the intersection of Mayfair and Speedway Avenues. The cars stream by all day, but few turn up Speedway, our quiet street. In front of our house is the place where we played touch football all summer and fall. Now the snow-covered street is deserted, and even the houses look cold.

WRITING PROJECTS 1. Develop a paragraph outline from one of the following topic sentences (or one of your own), making sure that every sentence supports the main idea. Indicate whether your paragraph will follow chronological order, order of importance, or spatial order.

I would never have guessed that our principal was right behind me.
It's no fun to be a stranger in a new school.
I talk too much.
Our lunch periods should be at least ten minutes longer.
Everything about the old house breathed mystery and decay.
The minute we opened our eyes, we knew it was going to be a day of great
excitement.
Sometimes I have a hard time understanding my parents.
In some ways, my room looks like me.
I remember the first time I saw my best friend.
Young people should have more responsibility.

2. Write a paragraph of 100 words, using the paragraph outline you developed in Exercise 1.

Tying Ideas Together

The main idea of a paragraph is stated in the topic sentence. The other sentences in the paragraph supply details which support the main idea, arranged in a suitable order. A well-constructed paragraph is not just a list of ideas, however. It ties all of them together so that the flow of thought is smooth and natural. Unless the paragraph does hang together, it is likely to be a tiresome experience for readers—and for the writer too!

BORING   Many railroads are in financial difficulties. Big trailer trucks carry much freight. More people own cars. Our highways have been greatly improved. The shortage of gasoline may help.

BETTER   Many railroads are in financial difficulties. Today, big trailer trucks carry much of the freight formerly hauled by the railroads. In addition, more people own cars than in the past, with the result that they now take advantage of our greatly improved highway system instead of riding the trains. However, the shortage of gasoline indirectly may aid the railroads by making gasoline-powered transportation so expensive that people and manufacturers will be forced to use the railroads.

In the first of these two paragraphs, the ideas are in a suitable order, but the writer has not taken the trouble to show the readers how they fit together. The real work of organizing the paragraph effectively has been left to the readers. In contrast, the second paragraph uses words, phrases, and a clause to tie all the details up in a neat, tight package. The expressions that connect the parts of the paragraph, underlined in red, are called *transitions*. They are the mortar that binds paragraphs together in a strong whole.

Transitional Words and Phrases The word *transition* comes from a Latin word which means "going across." A transition is a bridge linking sentences and ideas together. Some common transitional words are:

however	furthermore	besides
therefore	then	nevertheless

Some common transitional phrases are:

for example   on the contrary   as a result

Like all language tools, the transitional words should not be overused. A paragraph peppered with *therefore*'s is not very interesting.

Sentences That Look Backward and Forward Sentences of this sort link an idea presented in the preceding sentence with an idea that will be developed in later sentences. Such sentences are easy to construct by means of adverb clauses.

EXAMPLE   We must decide whether to have a class dance this year. **Although a dance is the traditional form for our party,** many of our dances have not been very successful.

Notice that the clause printed in red refers back to the previous sentence. The rest of the sentence introduces a new fact.

Repetition   Another way to build a bridge from one idea to another is by repeating key words.

EXAMPLE   Last winter's deep snow was very hard on the **deer** in the northern part of the state. These **deer**, which normally live in the woods, were observed on farms and even in towns, looking for food.

EXERCISE   Read each numbered sentence twice, first with sentence A after it and then with sentence B. In the blank to the left, write the letter of the sentence that fits in more smoothly with the numbered sentence.

.... 1. Some people consider a rainy day a terrible waste of time.
A. Some people like a rainy day.
B. On the contrary, a rainy day is ideal for reading, studying, or listening to music.

.... 2. Most young people are law-abiding and try hard to be a credit to their community.
A. It is a mistake, therefore, to judge all young people by the actions of a few juvenile delinquents.
B. There are not really very many juvenile delinquents.

.... 3. We are studying everyday German life in our German class.
A. To get firsthand information, we are writing to pen pals.
B. Since several members of the class have pen pals in Germany, we are going to write letters to them.

.... 4. My mother says that the teachers who taught her the most were the ones who expected the most of her.
A. My manual-training teacher does not expect much of me.
B. She admits, however, that she wasn't always fond of them at the time.

.... 5. When we learn to read, we begin with the alphabet.
A. In the same way, we begin the study of music with scales.
B. In music, we begin with scales.

244   © 1982 HBJ

Writing a Narrative Paragraph

A narrative paragraph tells a story. It follows a natural sequence of events or actions.

The narrative paragraph may be a story of something that happened to you, or something that happened to someone you know. It may be a true story or a story you have made up.

The narrative paragraph is one of the most interesting paragraphs to write. We all have events which happen to us each day, and we often enjoy telling stories about them.

A good narrative paragraph tells us what happened, when it happened, and sometimes where it happened. It presents a story just as it took place in time.

EXAMPLE

GWENETH

Opening sentence

After class, on wet winter days, I would trail along behind Gweneth to the bus stop, pause near the steps while she entered, and follow her down the aisle until she chose a seat. Usually, however, in clear violation of the code of conduct to which all gentlemen were expected to adhere, Leon Pugh would already be on the bus and shouting to passers-by, "Move off! Get away! This here seat by me is reserved for the girl from Brooklyn, New York." Discouraged but not defeated, I would swing into the seat nearest her and cast calf-eyed glances of wounded affection at the back of her head or at the brown, rainbow profile of her face. And at her stop, some eight or nine blocks from mine, I would disembark behind her along with a crowd of other love-struck boys. There would then follow a well-rehearsed scene in which all of us, save Leon Pugh, pretended to have gotten off the bus either too late or too soon to wend our proper paths homeward. And at slight costs to ourselves we enjoyed the advantage of being able to walk close by her as she glided toward her uncle's green-frame house. There, after pausing on the wooden steps and smiling radiantly around the crowd like a spring sun in that cold winter rain, she would sing, "Bye, y'all," and disappear into the structure with the mystery of a goddess. Afterward

Conclusion

I would walk away, but slowly, much slower than the other boys, warmed by the music and light in her voice against the sharp, wet winds of the February afternoon.[1]

[1]From *Elbow Room* by James Alan McPherson. Copyright © 1974 by James Alan McPherson. Reprinted by permission of Little, Brown and Company and Brandt & Brandt Literary Agents, Inc.

This narrative paragraph tells an incident in the writer's childhood. It carefully follows the order in which things happened: getting on the bus, getting off the bus, standing by Gweneth's house. It does not carelessly leave out any important facts or include any facts that do not belong in the story. The writer also chooses descriptive words such as "calf-eyed glances," and "the mystery of a goddess," which appeal to the reader's imagination.

When you write a narrative paragraph, keep these points in mind:

1. Make your topic sentence clear. Let it suggest the story you are about to tell.
2. Use as much detail as possible. Choose active, descriptive verbs.
3. Follow events just as they happen in time.
4. Give your paragraph a strong conclusion.

WRITING PROJECT Write a narrative paragraph (100–150 words.) Tell about something interesting that happened to you recently or choose one of the topics below. Before you begin writing, prepare a brief paragraph outline.

SUGGESTED
TOPICS

1. The day everything went wrong
2. The best way to kill time
3. How I stood one step from danger
4. The start of something special
5. A lucky break

Writing a Descriptive Paragraph

A descriptive paragraph uses details of sight, sound, touch, taste, or smell to give the reader the sense of what it would be like to "be there."

A descriptive paragraph uses details that appeal to the senses.

We all have occasion to describe things to people. When we go somewhere, a friend may ask what it was like in that place. The simple answer, "Oh, it was terrific!" is pleasant, but it is too broad and too lacking in details for anyone to understand what it was like. We experience the world through our five senses, and when we want to describe something, we must rely on those senses to communicate our impressions.

EXAMPLE   HOLMES VISITS THE PAWNBROKER

We traveled by the Underground as far as Aldersgate, and a short walk took us to Saxe-Coburg Square, the scene of the singular story which we had listened to in the morning. It was a *Visual details* poky, little, shabby-genteel place, where four lines of dingy two-storied brick houses looked out into a small railed-in enclosure where a lawn of weedy grass and a few clumps of faded *Atmosphere* laurel bushes made a hard fight against a smoke-laden and uncongenial atmosphere. Three gilt balls and a brown board with JABEZ WILSON in white letters, upon a corner house, announced the place where our red-headed client carried on his business. Sherlock Holmes stopped in front of it with his head on one side and looked it all over, with his eyes shining brightly between puckered lids. Then he walked slowly up the street, and then down again to the corner, still looking keenly at the houses. *Sounds* Finally he returned to the pawnbroker's, and, having thumped vigorously upon the pavement with his stick two or three times, he went up to the door and knocked. It was instantly opened by a bright-looking, cleanshaven young fellow, who asked him to step in.[1]

Arthur Conan Doyle uses very specific adjectives, such as "poky, little, shabby-genteel," "dingy two-storied," and "puckered." He also relies on colors, such as "brick," "gilt," and "brown." When Sherlock Holmes is introduced, we see each of his movements with great clarity. His head goes to one side, he walks slowly up and down the street, and he thumps "vigorously" on

---

[1]From "The Red-Headed League" from *The Great Adventures of Sherlock Holmes* by Sir Arthur Conan Doyle. Reprinted by permission of Simon & Schuster, Inc.

the pavement. All of these words appeal to our senses. A fine descriptive paragraph will often do exactly that.

When you write a descriptive paragraph, keep these points in mind:

1. The topic sentence tells what you are describing.
2. Try to see, hear, feel, taste, or smell what you are describing. Put these senses into words.
3. Include details of color, size, and number where possible.
4. Be sure to include enough details so that your reader can form a complete picture of what you describe.

WRITING PROJECT Write a descriptive paragraph (100–150 words). Describe something or someone you know very well or choose one of the topics below. Before you begin writing, prepare a brief paragraph outline.

SUGGESTED   1. The scariest house I've ever seen
TOPICS   2. A dinner I'll never forget
               3. There's one place where I can get away from it all
               4. Let it storm!
               5. On the street where I live

An expository paragraph explains *how, what,* or *why.* It often uses facts to inform the reader.

If you explain how earthquakes occur, you are being expository. If you explain what anchovies are, you are being expository. If you explain how to change a flat tire, you are being expository. The expository paragraph is the most common type of paragraph. You will find such paragraphs in newspapers, textbooks, manuals, and many other places. Because you are often asked to write expository paragraphs, you should know how to write them clearly.

Good expository paragraphs use specific information to support a single topic sentence.

EXAMPLE   THE LARGEST DINOSAUR

What was the largest animal that ever walked the earth? Scientists today believe it was a dinosaur whose bones were discovered in western Colorado. This creature, which lived some 140 million years ago, had a neck longer than 12 meters, had a body (excluding the neck) more than 24 meters in length, and probably weighed 80 tons. Scientists believe this monster was as tall as a six-story building. In spite of its size, scientists say, this largest of animals was a gentle plant-eater that walked on four legs with its neck upright (like a giraffe's) and fed from the high limbs of trees.

This paragraph gives information about the largest dinosaur that ever lived. It uses specific facts about physical characteristics to develop its topic. It answers a question. Notice that the first sentence asks a question; the rest of the paragraph answers it. Expository paragraphs do not always begin with a question. It is just one way you may begin. An expository paragraph usually has a topic sentence. In this example, the topic sentence is the second sentence in the paragraph.

When writing an expository paragraph, keep these points in mind:
1. The topic sentence establishes your subject and your approach.
2. Keep your sentences in a logical order.
3. Imagine you are answering a question for someone who wants to know *how, what,* or *why.*

Writing an Expository Paragraph

An expository paragraph explains *how, what,* or *why.* It often uses facts to inform the reader.

Expository paragraphs explain something to the reader.

If you explain how earthquakes occur, you are being expository. If you explain what anchovies are, you are being expository. If you explain how to change a flat tire, you are being expository. The expository paragraph is the most common type of paragraph. You will find such paragraphs in newspapers, textbooks, manuals, and many other places. Because you are often asked to write expository paragraphs, you should know how to write them clearly.

Good expository paragraphs use specific information to support a single topic sentence.

EXAMPLE   THE LARGEST DINOSAUR

What was the largest animal that ever walked the earth? Scientists today believe it was a dinosaur whose bones were discovered in western Colorado. This creature, who lived some 140 million years ago, had a neck longer than 12 meters, had a body (excluding the neck) more than 24 meters in length, and probably weighed 80 tons. Scientists believe this monster was as tall as a six-story building. In spite of its size, scientists say, this largest of animals was a gentle plant-eater that walked on four legs with its neck upright (like a giraffe's) and fed from the high limbs of trees.

This paragraph gives information about the largest dinosaur that ever lived. It uses specific facts about physical characteristics to develop its topic. It answers a question. Notice that the first sentence asks a question; the rest of the paragraph answers it. Expository paragraphs do not always begin with a question. It is just one way you may begin. An expository paragraph usually has a topic sentence. In this example, the topic sentence is the second sentence in the paragraph.

When writing an expository paragraph, keep these points in mind:

1. The topic sentence establishes your subject and your approach.
2. Keep your sentences in a logical order.
3. Imagine you are answering a question for someone who wants to know *how, what,* or *why.*

WRITING PROJECT   Write an expository paragraph (100–150 words). Prepare a paragraph outline before you begin. You may use a topic of your own or choose one of the topics below.

SUGGESTED
TOPICS

1. How to fix a _____
2. What is your least favorite day of the week?
3. Why is baseball (or any sport) the best sport?
4. How can your school improve its daily schedule?
5. What do you look for in a friend?
6. Why are clothes important in making an impression?

CHAPTER THIRTEEN

Writing Compositions and Letters

Like any important project, compositions require careful planning. The next six lessons of ENGLISH WORKSHOP will help you prepare for a variety of composition projects.

Letter writing is a crucial skill for communicating with friends and relatives and for entering a career. The last three lessons of ENGLISH WORKSHOP provide essential guidelines for successful letters.

LESSON 120

Selecting a Composition Subject

A skillful writer knows that only part of any large subject can be dealt with in a composition of only a few paragraphs. In a single paragraph, built around a single main idea, even less can be covered. Learning to *limit* a subject to a size that you can present effectively in the space available is an important part of learning to be a skillful writer.

After selecting a subject for a composition, limit it to an aspect that you can present effectively.

What makes a topic right for you? Keep these points in mind:

1. Know Your Subject You will do a better job on any composition or report when you write about a subject in which you have some interest and preferably some personal experience as well. (You will have more fun writing the composition, too.)

2. Have a Definite Point of View A story or essay with a distinct flavor of its own—humorous, mysterious, or exciting—is easier to write and more interesting to read than a theme in which you express no particular attitude. A definite point of view will help you to organize a report and keep it from being simply a collection of miscellaneous facts. Before you begin to write, ask yourself, "How do I feel about this subject? What do I think of it?"

The next step in planning a report or other composition is to narrow the topic down to a size that can be handled in the time and space assigned. You do this by breaking a large subject down into smaller parts, or *subtopics,* until you find one that fits.

LARGE TOPIC	*The Sea*

LARGE TOPIC   *The Sea*
(This topic is too broad for a short composition. It would take hundreds of volumes to cover it adequately.)

LARGE SUBTOPIC   *Life in the Sea*
(This topic is still too broad. It would fill several thick books.)

SMALLER SUBTOPIC   *Fishing*
(This would be a good topic for a long report, but it would require a good deal of library research to cover all kinds of fishing.)

STILL SMALLER   *Fishing in Sandcreek Bay*
(Because it is limited to one aspect of fishing, this subtopic would be good for a shorter composition.)

EXERCISE The following topics are too broad for a short composition. In the spaces on the right, below, suggest for each broad topic four limited subtopics which might make a good report or story. Notice the examples.

Baseball
1. *My Favorite Player*
2. *How Baseball Was Invented*
3. *The Most Exciting Game I Saw*
4. *My First Home Run*

Careers
1. ....
2. ....
3. ....
4. ....

Having a Good Time
1. ....
2. ....
3. ....
4. ....

Family Relationships
1. ....
2. ....
3. ....
4. ....

The Future
1. ....
2. ....
3. ....
4. ....

Planning a Composition

A mighty suspension bridge stretching out over a wide river or bay does not just happen. Years of careful planning by many people are behind its existence. A composition of several paragraphs does not just happen either. Like the bridge, all of its parts must fit together, each part helping to support the rest so that in its entirety it forms a solid, well-constructed whole.

In planning a composition, make notes on the points to be covered. Review your notes for order, completeness, and unity before you begin to write.

Suppose that you are planning a composition on the history of the town where you live. You jot down points in any order, as you think of them.

NOTES FOR A COMPOSITION
Early days—prosperous lumber industry
Today—fruit farming, paper, tourists
After lumber mills left, almost a ghost town
Grandfather Stanley's lumber mill

Are these all the points you want to cover? Is there anything on the list that does not belong? Probably you would not want to introduce anything as specific as your grandfather's lumber mill—it would throw the composition out of balance, spoiling its unity.

Are the composition's main points in the right order? Since you are writing about the town's history, time order is probably best. The third point—about what happened after the early lumbering days—is therefore out of place. Deciding on the right order also suggests another point that you did not think of when you jotted down your first notes—the Chinook village that stood where the town now is when the first settlers came. (In planning a longer composition, you will find it helpful to put your notes on separate slips of paper or on 3 x 5-inch cards. Then you can shift them around until you find the right order for the material.)

Here is the revised composition plan.

REVISED NOTES
Built where Chinook village once stood
At first, a prosperous lumber industry
Almost a ghost town after lumber mills left
Today—salt mining, fruit farming, paper, tourists

EXERCISE   Listed on page 254 are the first notes for three compositions. In the spaces at the right, rearrange them in the order that seems best to you, dropping out any items under a topic that would spoil the unity of the composition. Do your planning on a separate sheet of paper and be ready to discuss the order of points (time order, order of importance, space order) and your reasons for omitting any.

1. Topic: A Presidential election

   A. The election campaign   A. ....

   B. National convention of each   B. ....
      party

   C. Practices in other countries C. ....

   D. The electoral college   D. ....

   E. The popular vote   E. ....

2. Topic: Learning to play bridge

   A. Playing a hand   A. ....

   B. More interesting than rummy   B. ....

   C. Object of the game   C. ....

   D. Rules for scoring   D. ....

   E. Evaluating a hand   E. ....

3. Topic: Preventing traffic accidents

   A. Enforcing speed limits   A. ....

   B. Compulsory driver training   B. ....

   C. Revoking reckless drivers'   C. ....
      licenses

   D. Inspecting cars for defects   D. ....

   E. Periodic testing of drivers   E. ....

   F. Higher gasoline taxes   F. ....

MAKING AN OUTLINE

In getting ready to write about anything, we do just as much preplanning as the material requires—*but no more than that.* If the composition is likely to be long or complicated, it is generally worthwhile to make a detailed outline first.

Follow the standard outline form.

The composition notes on page 253 might well be developed into a full account of the town's history, in which each point is presented in a separate paragraph of its own.

The Town That Wouldn't Die

I. Early settlers
    II. Growth and decline of the lumber industry
A. Lumber barons
        B. Cut-over land
    III. New sources of wealth
        A. New industry
1. Salt mining   .
            2. Paper making
        B. Fruit farming
        C. Tourists
    IV. The town today

Notice the use of Roman numerals, capital letters, and Arabic numbers to show the relative importance of each point in the outline. Notice too that items of equal importance are all indented the same, so that we can see at a glance how the different parts of the outline fit together.

EXERCISE A   The following is an outline for a short composition. Several items have been omitted and are listed at the end of the outline. From these phrases, pick the one you think best fits in each blank space.

How to Prepare for a Test

 I. Review the textbook.

    A. ....

    B. Don't try to reread the whole book.
        1. You can't remember all the details.

        2. ....

 II. Review class notes.
    A. Think how they are related to the text.

    B. ....

III. Drill on material to be memorized.

    A. ....
    B. Get someone to test you.

IV. Get a good night's sleep.
    A. A sleepy student forgets things.

    B. ....

Drill yourself.
A sleepy student is slow.
Make note of the points the teacher emphasized.
List the most important points in each chapter of the textbook.
You don't have enough time.

255

EXERCISE B   Suppose you were writing a report on vitamin D and had made the following notes. On a separate sheet of paper, organize these notes into an outline for your report. Be sure to follow the standard outline form, using main topics, subtopics, and minor points.

Vitamin D is necessary to build good teeth and bones.

Absence of vitamin D may cause rickets.

Vitamin D is made by skin cells when summer sun shines on the skin.

Absence of vitamin D may cause poor tooth development.

Both children and adults need vitamin D.

Fish oils such as halibut oil and cod-liver oil are rich in vitamin D.

Vitamin D is also added to packaged foods such as homogenized milk and evaporated milk.

WRITING PROJECT   Plan and write a composition of several paragraphs on one of the subjects suggested below or another that you prefer. Make notes on the ideas you want to include and arrange them in an effective order. Develop your notes into a complete outline following the standard form and hand the outline in to your teacher with the finished composition.

Growing up is a painful process
A favorite historical character
Physical fitness is fun
Flying saucers really exist
Joining a rock band

Reasons for (against) television
The trouble with student government
Observing nature near home
Country music is my kind of music
Mental telepathy—fact or fiction?

Writing Means Rewriting

The compositions you submit to a teacher or ask anyone else to read represent *you.* They should be as good as you can make them. Often, in order to make a piece of writing as good as it really can be, you must write parts of it a second time as well as make simple corrections in grammar and sentence structure. It is often a good idea to reread a first draft several times, systematically, like a professional proofreader, each time looking for a different kind of weakness. Only then are you ready to make a correct, final copy of your composition.

Reread a first draft for meaning.

Ask yourself questions like these:
1. Does my writing say what I want it to say? Is it convincing?
2. Have I developed parts of my composition too much? too little? Should any part be expanded or shortened?
3. Are there awkward breaks in the flow of ideas? Are any ideas out of place? Should any sentences or paragraphs be moved to a later or an earlier point?

Pay special attention to the beginning and ending of a composition—its *introduction* and *conclusion.* The introduction affects readers' attitudes toward what follows and should give them an idea of the scope of your composition and the approach you are taking. The conclusion determines your readers' final impressions. It should summarize the points you want to stay in their minds.

Reread a first draft for sentence structure and variety.

Compare these two versions of the same composition:

FIRST DRAFT
Scientists have discovered new bacteria. They are very helpful. They can turn refuse into protein. A food product that is high in this protein can be manufactured. Scientists hope to feed this food product to cows and hogs. Perhaps someday people will eat it too.

REVISION
Beware—your garbage can may contain the food of the future. After years of research, scientists have discovered bacteria capable of turning common garbage into a protein substance. This substance is the base of a new food that scientists plan to feed to cows and hogs. If ways of making the substance more appetizing are found, people soon may be eating their garbage. Can you imagine a cookbook on twelve ways of preparing garbage, trash, and refuse?

Reading a composition aloud will often help you to spot faults in sentence structure. Notice how the revision has gotten away from the short, choppy simple sentences of the first draft. The revised opening for the paragraph is much stronger than the original. It catches the reader's interest by telling immediately, in one sentence, the important thing that the paragraph has to say

Reread a first draft for errors in mechanics.

The part of writing called *mechanics* is concerned with all those things that we ought to know so well that we do them automatically—*punctuation, capitalization,* and *spelling.*

EXERCISE A On a separate sheet of paper, revise each of the following paragraphs so that it shows a good development of ideas, with proper transitional devices, and an interesting variation in sentence structure.

1. I have always been interested in studying the Civil War. My grandmother used to tell me about it. Her mother told her. General William Sherman was near our farm. We have pictures of soldiers in blue uniforms. My great- great-grandfather knew General P. T. Beauregard. It is fascinating to see what happened in the great battles. We visited Bull Run when we went to Washington last year. It is also called Manassas. I stood on the ridge and looked at the stone farmhouse in the distance. I almost thought I could see a gray line of troops emerging from the woods.

2. Interlochen is a camp in northern Michigan. It is an unusual camp. Its campers spend the summer studying music. Students come from all over the country. Some come from foreign countries. The motto of Interlochen is: "Dedicated to the promotion of world friendship through the universal language of the arts." Students at Interlochen also have time to go fishing and swimming. A concert is given every week. The very youngest campers are eight years old. Many are university students.

3. Every living creature has a life cycle. A honeybee lives only about five weeks. Some one-celled bacteria live only twenty minutes or half an hour. Turtles may live for a hundred years. The oldest living things on earth are trees. Some of the giant redwood trees in California are more than two thousand years old. People and elephants may also live to be a hundred. During a lifetime, living things go through similar processes of birth, growth, reproduction, and death. Fruit flies live for only one month.

4. Everyone needs food for energy. A calorie is a scientific term used to measure heat energy. Body cells use the energy stored in food to do their work, and the energy in food is measured in calories. Very active people need more calories than less active people do. An hour of sleeping uses 65 calories. An

hour of swimming uses 430 calories. An hour's leisurely walk requires 110 calories. A large apple would furnish enough energy to walk for an hour, and a malted milk enough energy to swim for an hour. Our bodies use calories for every activity.

EXERCISE B The following paragraphs contain errors in subject and verb agreement, modifier usage, punctuation, capitalization and spelling. Proofread the paragraphs and write in the correction above each error. Add capitals, apostrophes, quotation marks, and other end marks wherever necessary. Cross out any misspelled or incorrectly used word and write the correct word above it. Be sure to correct sentence fragments and run-ons.

1. I have a new hobby of making mosaics, it is a lot of fun. I got interested in mosaics when I received a kit for my birthday. The first thing I made was a bowl. Which I hope to give my Mother for her Birthday.

Would you like to know how to make mosaics. First you spread a thin layer of mortar on the place you want to decorate. Then you arrange the little tiles the way they look best to you. After the mortar have dried you put the grout between the tiles. Its a white paste. Be sure to clean off all the grout from the tiles before its dry. If you been careful, it looks nicely. I tried to teach Vic my second cousin. But he dont have the patiance.

2. I asked Mrs. Habeeb our next-door neighbor how it felt to be a hundred years old. I guess I must have been the hundredth person to ask her. "Its a nuisance she admitted all you people around with you're questions". She relented a little. "Well young fellow" she asked. "Dont you want to know what I think"? I said I did of course. "I think", she pronounced as slowly and as firmly as her cracked voice would let her. "Id like to turn around and start getting younger."

3. Many kinds of vaccine is used to protect people from diseases. Diphtheria whooping cough lockjaw smallpox polio, and rubella all has vaccines and scientists are working on vaccines for still other diseases. When a vaccine is introduced into the body the cells forms antibodies. It is these antibodies which fight off the actual disease germs. A vaccination for example is a small dose of a cowpox virus a variety of the dreaded smallpox. You were probaly vaccinated before you were a year old at that time the cowpox virus caused your body to produce antibodies which fight against smallpox. These anti-

bodies stay with you for many years. If you were ever to get smallpox. It would probaly be a very mild case.

4. Connie likes to read the dictionary. Can you imagine that. Sometimes I see her settle down in her favorite chair by the fireplace. Whenever shes really tired she reaches for our dictionary then she flips it open to any page and starts to read. I dont read straight through from beginning to end she told me once but I flip to a certain page and just browse up and down. She says that she has discuvered many fascinating words. She also likes to read the word historyes which are part of the entrys. Connie is very generous with her discoveries and likes to share them with anyone who will listen. Do you know what an auklet is she called to me last night. Its a small auk a diving bird which lives in the arctic lands. I have to admit that Connies hobby has made her a whiz at crossword puzles.

Writing a Descriptive Composition

An effective description can make readers see the thing it pictures as clearly and vividly as if they were there themselves. Like a good snapshot, a description focuses on a single point of interest. It keeps out details that are not important to the main impression that the writer is trying to create. A description also has something which a photograph does not have—the writer's particular viewpoint or way of looking at things.

In writing a description, concentrate on showing your readers how the thing you describe looks to you.

Notice the ways Anne Morrow Lindbergh creates a clear and vivid picture of a herd of elephants:

EXAMPLE   We see elephants in the evening on approaching our first campsite beside a dry riverbed. The pale dusty track angles in on our right, a luminous stream of sand pockmarked by animal hooves. Leaving our Land-Rover on a bank, we walk out onto the dry bed. We look both ways, and stop. Downriver stands a cliff of elephants—dark, enormous, motionless, their tree-sized legs rooted in sand, their ears widespread, great trunks facing us, white tusks gleaming in the dusk. They sway now, and blow dust from their sinuous trunks, huge ears flapping gently as palm fronds. They begin to move in single file along the bank, great shadows melting in and out of trees. In no hurry, they move deliberately, picking up one muffled foot after another with noiseless grace. We stand silently mid-river and watch the procession march in solemn rhythm, as if keeping time to inaudible drums.

Late in the evening, we hear them at the muddy pool across the river from our tent. They are pawing at the ground with ponderous feet to reach new water. They slosh in the mud and spray each other with their trunks. In the moonlight we can dimly see their hulking shapes; as we hear the water on their dusty hides, we feel ourselves a part of their joy.[1]

1. The passage describes the elephants *in a setting*. It tells us the place (on a dry riverbed) and the time of day (evening).

2. The passage is *unified*. It tells us nothing that does not relate to the elephants and the setting in which they are seen.

[1] From *Earth Shine* by Anne Morrow Lindbergh. Copyright © 1966, 1969 by Anne Morrow Lindbergh. Reprinted by permission of Harcourt Brace Jovanovich, Inc.

3. The passage uses *carefully chosen words* that make us see and hear the elephants just as they looked and sounded to the author. For example, the legs of the elephants are *tree-sized,* but as they walk they are silent, *picking up one muffled foot after another with noiseless grace.* What other details describe how the elephants looked and sounded?

EXERCISE   The sentences below all describe something, but they do so in flat, dull words that do not create a clear picture in readers' minds. Choose any five of the sentences that tell about things that you have seen or remember vividly. Then on a separate piece of paper rewrite the sentences, using words that tell clearly how each thing described looks to you. Concentrate on using precise and descriptive nouns and verbs. Do not use two adjectives or adverbs where one will do.

1. The small house was hidden among vines and oak trees.
2. Fresh snow covered the mountain village.
3. There is a bridge over the brook near our farm.
4. I saw a deer come over a hedge and run away.
5. After the rain, the clouds moved away and a rainbow appeared.
6. The dog was small and fat and too old to be playful.
7. Deep pools catch the water from the falls.
8. The bacon was cooking in the frying pan.
9. The girl dived from the dock and swam toward the raft.
10. The new car was standing in the driveway.

WRITING PROJECT   Write a description of 150–200 words about one of the subjects suggested below or one of your own choosing. Keep these points in mind.

1. Limit your description to a few clear details that will show your readers how the thing described looked to you.
2. Show the thing in its setting—time and place.
3. Use words that will tell your readers how the things looked (or felt, smelled, tasted, or sounded) to you.

SUBJECTS FOR A DESCRIPTION

1. Something you saw on the way to school
2. Something you can see from your desk or classroom window
3. Your favorite person or place
4. The house or apartment building where you live
5. A park or field near your home
6. A lunch counter or drugstore

Writing a Narrative Composition

You probably know someone who possesses the ability to make the simplest story totally entertaining. The same story or joke, dealt with by someone else, might well fail to entertain at all. What is the difference between these two people? Good storytellers, either consciously or instinctively, know how to organize their material. Poor storytellers do not. They add unnecessary comments, so that you wonder if they will ever come to the point. Or else they give away the punch line ahead of time.

1. Plan the Plot of Your Story Writing a story, either true or fictional, has a lot in common with telling a joke or an anecdote. Its effectiveness depends on the way it is organized. All stories have a *plot,* a plan of action or events. When you are going to write or tell a story, work out the plot first.

2. Capture the Reader's Interest Your first sentence might contain description, conversation, or action. The story you are telling determines which is most suitable. If you are telling a story where the personalities of the characters are important, a line or two of conversation is an excellent way to show what kind of people they are. If action is important, a brief, sharp incident makes a strong beginning. When surroundings have a bearing on the story or a definite mood is necessary, you can start with description.

3. Create Suspense Many stories are written in time order, telling what happened first, then what happened next. This avoids giving away what happens at the end. You can also help to create suspense by letting your readers know something the main character is not aware of or by putting in a fact which is not important at the moment but which is necessary to make the climax convincing. This is called *foreshadowing.* Move quickly along the sequence of events until you reach the *climax,* or most important part of the story. The climax is the point where the action of the story must turn out one way or the other. After the climax briefly explain any minor items that need to be cleared up and end the story.

4. Make the Story Believable To be believable, a story's characters must act as real people would under the circumstances you have created for them. Conversation also makes a story realistic, as readers can "hear" people talking and so feel themselves more a part of what is taking place. Careful rewriting for specific verbs and good description also adds to a story's realism.

5. Use Dialogue When Possible Good writers reproduce conversation the way people usually speak it, in short spurts rather than long speeches. They are also careful to give their dialogue variety by devising different ways to indicate who is speaking. Here are some of the many synonyms for *said.*

added	denied	murmured	replied
asked	drawled	observed	shouted
begged	explained	offered	whimpered
demanded	insisted	repeated	whispered

Each synonym tells something different about the way people speak.

EXAMPLES   "But I've already told you," Douglas shouted.
"But I've already told you," insisted Douglas.
Douglas murmured, "But I've already told you."

The suggestions above can be put to work even in telling a very simple incident like the following. Notice how the story builds up to its climax. Notice also how much of the story is told through dialogue.

HIDDEN TREASURE

In the fall, we moved to Elm Street, into an old house which my father enthusiastically described as "authentic Victorian." Aunt Sue, Uncle Warren, and my cousin May came over to help us unpack and clean up. May and I drew the basement. Shelf after shelf was packed with jars and old paint cans, and we were loading the cans into boxes and carting them out for the junk collector.

"They must have been in the old paint-can *business,*" May complained. "Why couldn't they clean the place up before they moved out?"

"Make 'em into lamps," I suggested cheerfully. "Soup kettles. Buckets. Where's your ingenuity? You could make your fortune."

"Hold it! Hold everything," said May abruptly. "What is it?" At the back of a shelf she had uncovered a rusty tin box fastened with a small padlock. When she gave it a shake, there was a dry, whispering sound from within.

"Money!" we both shouted together. "We're rich!"

We found a screwdriver and went to work. The padlock wouldn't budge, but the hinges at the back were easier. After fifteen minutes of effort, we had pried the box open. It was packed with old bills in neat piles—hundreds, fifties, tens.

"Wow!" May exploded. "Just look at it! Thousands—millions!"

"Too bad it isn't real." I laughed the dry little chuckle that I had been practicing lately and picked up a wad of the stuff. "Monopoly money," I explained with precision, "you know, the game. Now, shall we get back to work?"

WRITING PROJECT Write a narrative of 200–250 words, either real or imaginary, about a situation suggested by one of the following topics. You may make up a situation of your own.

Marcia's big day	Tony and the galloping ghost
Sink or swim	Space police
The great mix-up	Hobnobbing with hobbits
The mysterious noises	The bench warmer

Writing an Expository Composition

The expository composition, like the expository paragraph, presents useful or interesting information to the reader about a single topic.

An expository composition explains something to the reader. It is divided into introduction, body, and conclusion.

Planning an expository composition is extremely important. Selecting and narrowing your topic, deciding the purpose of your composition, and outlining your ideas should all be done before you begin writing.

An expository composition has three basic parts: the introduction, the body, and the conclusion. The introduction (usually the first paragraph) should prepare the reader for what follows. It should state the topic and the purpose of the composition.

The body is the middle of the composition. It develops the composition topic by use of specific information. How long should the body be? It should be long enough to develop fully the composition topic. It is usually two or more paragraphs.

The conclusion should summarize the topic and the main points. It should tie the composition together. Conclusions are best when they are brief (usually one paragraph).

EXAMPLE

LOST!

Introduction   If you are hiking in the woods and become lost, you will need to know how to find your way out of danger. When lost, many foolish hikers wander aimlessly or scream loudly, but these methods often result in exhaustion, not rescue. You are more likely to regain your sense of direction by using a few simple techniques practiced by experienced hikers.

Body   Your first guide should be your own eyes. Climb a tree or other high lookout point and scan the horizon for recognizable landmarks: a road, a river, a house, or another high peak. Your second guide should be your compass. By plotting a course in one direction and consulting your compass regularly, you can make progress toward safety.

If, however, dense fog or rain creates low visibility or if you do not have a compass, don't panic. Sit down and think for a moment, try to relax, and try to remember the direction in which you came. Keeping a cool head and making clear judgments will prevent you from rushing off in a haphazard, possibly wrong direction.

Try to be 100 percent sure of the way back before attempting to retrace your steps. If you are uncertain, tie a flag to a tree or some high point and walk a circle around the flag, moving as far away as you can while still keeping the flag in sight. You may, as you circle the flag, stumble across the trail back.

Conclusion   When one is lost in the woods, it is never enough simply to wait for rescue. Do everything you can to attract notice. Build a bright fire at night or a smoky fire during the day. Use bright colors, shiny metal, or a flashing mirror to signal aircraft. Above all, try to rescue yourself by doggedly searching for the way back.

WRITING PROJECT   Write an expository composition (200–250 words). Before you begin writing, choose and narrow your own composition topic or choose one of the topics listed below. Prepare an outline of your ideas. Be sure your composition has an introduction, body, and conclusion. After you finish writing, proofread your composition for errors in mechanics. Hand in your composition outline along with your composition.

SUGGESTED TOPICS   1. Television without advertising
2. A summer holiday for my family
3. How I would change the rules
4. Choosing a career
5. The finest rock (soul, etc.) musicians

Writing About Books

In a written book report, you give much the same information that you give in recommending a book to a friend. Since your opinion of the book is important, organize a book report as you would any other theme that presents ideas.

In a book report, support your opinion with facts and with examples from the book.

A book report need not be long—a single paragraph will often do the job effectively. In your own book reports, try to cover the points suggested below, though not always in the order in which they are listed here. Notice how the outline for a report on fiction (novels and stories) differs from the one on nonfiction (history, biography, and other books that present facts).

Book Report on Fiction

1. Give the title and author of the book and indicate its general nature (adventure or mystery story, historical novel, etc.).

2. Mention the main characters briefly and tell how they fit into the story.

3. Summarize the main conflict or problem and tell a little about the plot *without* giving away the ending.

4. Give your opinion of the book. (Did you like it? Will others enjoy it?)

Book Report on Nonfiction

1. Give the title and author of the book and tell what kind of book it is (history, true narrative, biography, etc.).

2. Describe the subject of the book.

3. Summarize the information presented in the book.

4. Give your opinion of the book. (What did you learn from it? Was it clearly and enjoyably written?)

Keep these general suggestions in mind in all of your book reports:

1. Tell one or two high points of the book and give examples to show why you did (or did *not*) like it. Do not try to tell all about the book or your report will get bogged down in details.

2. Do not be vague in giving your opinion. Think about your reasons for liking or disliking the book and about the reasons your readers might have for reading it also. It is far more useful to know that a book about World War II was so vivid it was like living through the experiences yourself than simply that it was "very interesting."

Notice how the suggestions given above are applied in the following two book reports.

Peter Benchley's novel *Jaws* tells the story of a shark that menaces a Long Island sea resort and the terror that it brings with it. When the shark first attacks, the residents of the town are faced with a dilemma: Should they warn the tourists of the danger and face the inevitable loss of business that the town so badly needs, or should they remain silent and hope that the shark will not strike again? Finally the town is forced to hunt the shark. The description of the hunt is one of the most exciting things I have ever read. I like the book because the people and their adventures seem so real and so thrilling. I would recommend it to anyone who enjoys books of adventure and suspense.

LIVING THROUGH D-DAY

The Longest Day by Cornelius Ryan is an hour-by-hour history of D-day, the day on which the Allies invaded occupied Europe in World War II. The author interviewed hundreds of veterans on both sides of the battle and has combined their stories in a single exciting narrative. I had read about World War II in our history textbook, but it never seemed so vivid or important to me until I read this book. From it, you learn what the soldiers who took part had for breakfast, what they were thinking about, the jokes they made, and the songs they sang. Reading *The Longest Day* is like living through D-day yourself but seeing it from all sides as those who were in it never could.

WRITING PROJECT Write a book report on a book you have recently read and enjoyed. Be sure your report tells the name of the book, its author, and the chief characters. If you summarize the plot, be sure to leave your readers in suspense as to the outcome. If the book is nonfiction, give a general idea of the material covered, and, if possible, tell one interesting incident or idea in some detail. Give concrete reasons for your opinion of the book.

Writing Social Letters

Although everyone enjoys receiving letters, many people find writing them a chore. With a little practice and the information in this lesson, you should find that composing a friendly letter is easy and fun.

The simplest part of writing a letter, but one that gives some people the most trouble, is the form which it should take. There are a few easy rules about the form of a friendly letter.

Write friendly letters neatly on stationery which is in good taste.

This rule is only common sense. Nobody wants to receive a letter in which the handwriting is so bad that it cannot be read. Perfumed letters are always in poor taste and leave the recipient open to teasing. Paper in white or very light colors is always acceptable, and blue or black ink is the most legible.

Do not use lined paper. If your handwriting tends to run up or downhill, you can place a sheet of heavily lined paper under the sheet you are writing on to guide you. Many letter tablets come with a sheet for this purpose.

Follow the generally accepted form for a social letter.

1. The *heading* is your own address and today's date. Its usual position is in the upper right-hand corner of the page. It tells where and when the letter was written. Notice that there is a comma between the date of the month and the year and between the city and the state. There is no comma between the state and the zip code. There are no periods. If you are writing a letter to a very close friend who knows your address, or if you are using stationery with your address printed on it, the date alone is sufficient.

1. Heading

225 Jackson Road
Baltimore, Maryland 21222
August 20, 1981

2. Salutation

Dear Rinaldo,

3. Body

4. Closing
5. Signature

Your friend,
Peter

A Model for Social Letter Form

2. The *salutation* begins at the left-hand margin and is placed slightly below the heading. It is followed by a comma. Most letters should begin with "Dear" and the name of the person you are writing to, but some people prefer to say something slightly different, like "Hi, Mary."

3. The *body* of a friendly letter is the message. It usually starts out indented like a paragraph. Other paragraphs in the letter are indented the same distance.

4. Use one of the following *closings* for a friendly or social letter. (Do not use *Yours truly,* or *Very truly yours.* These closings are used only in business letters.)

CLOSINGS   Sincerely,   As ever,
                   Sincerely yours,   Affectionately,
                   Your friend,   Love,
                   Best wishes to all,   Regards,

Notice that the first word in a closing phrase is capitalized. The phrase is placed just below the final line of the letter, beginning a little to the right of the middle of the page, and is followed by a comma.

5. The *signature* in a friendly letter is usually just your first name. Center it under the closing, and always write it by hand, even if you have typed the rest of the letter.

EXERCISE   The outlined space below represents a piece of stationery. Write the heading for a letter of your own. Use your own address and today's date. In the appropriate place, write a salutation and punctuate it properly. Do not write the body of the letter. Add a closing and position it properly. Then sign your name to the letter.

A good letter tells what the writer is doing and thinking about. It is like a visit with an absent friend. Because it is meant for only one person, it also considers what the recipient might be doing or thinking, and it often asks questions. These should be specific questions which show that the letter writer is really thinking of the friend. "Did you ever catch that big fish in the pool below the dam?" shows that the writer recalls the friend's desire or attempt to catch the fish. A letter that merely goes through the motions of inquiring ("I am fine. How are you?") is a bore.

In addition to the friendly letter, which is written to tell news and to keep up a friendship, there is another kind of letter you may wish to write occasionally. This is the *thank-you note*.

When you have received a gift or favor from someone whom you cannot thank immediately in person, write a thank-you note. Always do it promptly. If you delay, the giver will think the gift did not arrive or that you did not like it. Make your letter sound as though you are sincerely pleased and grateful. A sentence or two about how you plan to use the gift is thoughtful.

A THANK-YOU NOTE

101 Cole Avenue
Mansfield, Ohio 44902
August 20, 1981

Dear Aunt Bettina,

Your package arrived this morning, and opening it was even more exciting than my birthday party yesterday. How did you know I've been dreaming of owning a real riding outfit? It's beautiful, and I've been parading around in it all afternoon. I can hardly wait for my riding lesson on Saturday. I'll bet the horses will have more respect for me now!

Give my love to Uncle Tom and Nancy and Frank. And thanks again for the wonderful gift.

Love, *Christie*

WRITING PROJECT Choose one of the situations below and write an appropriate letter. Try to project your own personality in the writing, and observe the correct form. Make up names and incidents to make the letter seem realistic.

1. Your grandmother has sent you a puppy for Christmas or Chanukah.
2. Write a letter to a friend who has just moved to a distant city.
3. From an aunt and uncle who live in a distant city, you received a very fine tennis racket as a birthday gift. (You may substitute something else you would like that might reasonably be given as a birthday gift.)
4. Your sister, who is studying music in Paris, has sent you a dress from a famous French fashion house. Write to tell her how excited and pleased you are.
5. While your neighbors were away, you took care of their dog. They gave you two tickets to the football game to thank you for the favor. Write a note to express your gratitude for the tickets.

Writing Business Letters

Even people who are not in business find reasons for writing business letters. They order something from a catalogue or a magazine. They write away for information which they may need for their schoolwork, or they send something back to a factory for repair.

As your responsibilities increase, you will have more and more occasions for writing business letters. The people who answer letters in business firms are very busy. They do not have time to decipher a messy letter or to read through a vague, rambling one. A good business letter should be correct in form and contain only the necessary information, clearly stated. Notice that a business letter differs from a friendly letter in its inside address, salutation, and closing.

1. **Heading**

2. **Inside Address**

3. **Salutation**

4. **Body**

5. **Closing**

6. **Signature**

> 52 Morse Avenue
> Erie, Pennsylvania 16511
> October 2, 1981
>
> Annie Rowe Candy Company
> 1720 Sawyer Avenue
> Chicago, Illinois 60623
>
> Gentlemen:
>
>   Please send me a two-pound box of your black-walnut chocolates. I am enclosing a check for $3.87, which you advise me will cover the cost of the candy and postage.
>
>   Yours truly,
>
> *Elizabeth Calkins*
>
> (Miss) Elizabeth Calkins

A Model for Business Letter Form

1. The *heading* of a business letter is the same as for a friendly letter. It contains your address and the date. However, if your paper has a printed letterhead, write only the date.

2. The *inside address* is an exact copy of the outside address on the envelope. It is used only in business letters.

3. The *salutation* in a business letter is followed by a colon, not a comma.

If the inside address begins with the name of an individual within a company, the salutation is *Dear* followed by the person's name (Dear Mr. Perkins: Dear Ms. Warberg:).

If the letter is addressed to an official in the firm whose name you do not know (Sales Manager, Director), you have a choice of salutations (Dear Sir: Dear Madame: Dear Sales Manager:).

If the letter is addressed to a company in general (Wisconsin Trust Company, Multispeed Bicycle Company), use either Gentlemen: or Dear Sirs: as the salutation. (It should be understood that there may be both men and women in the company.)

4. For the *body* of the letter, double space between paragraphs if you are using a typewriter. In typing, the paragraphs are usually indented five spaces.

5. Capitalize only the first word of the *closing* and use a comma after it. Suitable closings are:

> Yours truly,
> Very truly yours,
> Yours sincerely,
> Sincerely yours,

6. There are certain rules for the *signature* of a business letter. Never put a title (Mr. Mrs. Miss, etc.) before your handwritten signature. If you have typed the letter, type your name below your signature so that the company can be sure of the spelling.

Harriet Stewart

Harriet Stewart

EXERCISE Correct the following business letter form by inserting or crossing out punctuation marks and capitals where necessary. If the wording is incorrect, cross out the incorrect words and supply an appropriate word or words. (Add 10 points for each correct answer.)

1 153 Fiske Avenue

2 Boston Massachusetts 02189

3 June 1 1981

4   Brent's Sporting Goods Company,

5   101 Roselle Avenue,

6   Akron Ohio, 44307

7   Dear sir,

8   Your friend,

9   Sandra

In a business letter, be clear, courteous, and brief.

If your parents send you to the store for a loaf of bread and a pound of margarine and you come home without the bread, or with butter instead of margarine, you can hop on your bicycle and go back to the store to correct your mistake or omission. However, if you order an item by mail and fail to include all the necessary information, you will receive something you do not want. Correcting the mistake will involve sending back the merchandise, another exchange of letters, and considerable delay. It is important that your business letters furnish all the necessary information and that this information be expressed clearly and concisely.

It is also important to write courteously, even if the purpose of your letter is to express dissatisfaction. A rude letter makes a bad impression and gets few results. Business letters should also be brief. A company that sells exclusively by mail, for instance, receives thousands of letters every day. Its order clerks would not only waste time but might also be confused by an overly long letter.

The two most common types of business letters are order letters and request letters.

Order Letters

1. Identify the merchandise ordered by giving its catalogue number or by referring to an advertisement, and by giving its price. If size, color, or other information is necessary, be sure it is included.
2. State how the merchandise is to be paid for (check, money order, or COD—"cash on delivery").

Request Letters

1. State clearly what you are asking for (information, a catalogue, or free samples, etc.). Study the model on page 276.
2. If what you want is not offered in the company's advertising, give the reason for your request. If you have seen the offer in an advertisement, state where you saw it.
3. Express thanks or appreciation, since you are asking a favor. The thanks should not be used as a closing phrase, but should appear in the body of the letter.

WRITING PROJECT Choose one of the situations described below and write an appropriate letter. Be sure to observe the correct form for a business letter. Identify exactly what you want, and, if you are ordering an item, tell how it is to be paid for. Do not mail any letter without the approval of your teacher.

1. You notice in your local newspaper that the Lee Pen Company at 19 Clancy Avenue in Flint, Michigan 48503, is offering twenty ballpoint pens for $6.00 if all are ordered with the same color of ink.
2. Your French teacher suggests that you contact the French Government Tourist Office at 610 Fifth Avenue, New York, New York 10020, for free travel posters and maps of the various regions of France.

```
                              53 Lark Circle
                              Ogden, Utah 84403
                              March 27, 1981

     Director of Public Relations
     Ranger Bicycle Company
     227 Roper Road
     Duluth, Minnesota 55804

     Dear Sir:

         I read in last month's Bicycle World that your
     company has an excellent collection of antique
     bicycles.  For my social studies class, I am writing
     a report on bicycles as transportation.  If you
     have any free printed matter, particularly with
     pictures, which describes your collection, I would
     greatly appreciate receiving a copy.

                              Yours sincerely,

                              John A. Olson

                              John A. Olson
```

A Model Request Letter

Follow the accepted form for envelopes.

```
     John A. Olson
     53 Lark Circle
     Ogden, Utah 84403

                    Director of Public Relations
                    Ranger Bicycle Company
                    227 Roper Road
                    Duluth, Minnesota 55804
```

A Model Envelope

Practice in Letter Writing

BUSINESS LETTERS Choose one of the following situations and write the letter it requires, using a separate sheet of paper. (Make up any details you may need, including a complete address.)

1. Your parents have told you that you may go to camp next year. In a magazine you noticed an advertisement for a camp in Colorado which emphasizes your favorite hobby, horseback riding. Your father suggests that you write the camp director about rates, requirements, and transportation.
2. You have bought a model airplane kit from a local hobby shop and have discovered that it was packed without the instruction sheet. The store owner does not have any extras and suggests that you write Gem Plastic Products, 39 Grand Ave., Louisville, Kentucky 40201, for an instruction sheet to go with the model kit you bought.
3. You have been delegated by your class to make arrangements for a class tour of a nearby plant which makes yogurt.
4. You have decided to order a gift subscription to your parents' favorite magazine for their anniversary gift. (Choose a real magazine and get the correct information from its contents page.)
5. Your ambition is to see a television show. Since your family will be in the city where a certain program originates, you want to write the broadcasting company requesting tickets for the broadcast of a particular date. (Use a real program.)
6. You have decided to write a letter to the editor of your local newspaper. You want to suggest that a traffic light be put up at a busy intersection near your school where two pedestrians have been injured during the past year.

SOCIAL LETTERS Choose one of the following situations and write the letter it requires, using a separate sheet of paper. (Supply any details which you may need, including a complete address.)

1. You have a pen pal in England who, like you, is interested in stamp collecting. You have recently received a letter from him or her which included several new stamp issues. You plan to send your pen pal duplicates of American commemoratives.
2. For your birthday, a distant relative has sent you a book which is about your favorite sport. You have already read two chapters and are writing to thank him or her.
3. Your friend at school has been ill, but is now on the road to recovery. You want to give him or her the news about what is going on in your class.

The United States Postal Service recommends the use of two-letter codes for states, the District of Columbia, and Puerto Rico. The Service also recommends the use of nine-digit zip codes. When including these codes, the address should look like this:

EXAMPLE   Ms. Rita McNally
4025 Birch Ave.
Sacramento, CA 95825-2323

The following is a list of two-letter codes for states, the District of Columbia, and Puerto Rico. Notice that the codes do not include periods.

Alabama AL	Louisiana La	Ohio OH
Alaska AK	Maine ME	Oklahoma OK
Arizona AZ	Maryland MD	Oregon OR
Arkansas AR	Massachusetts MA	Pennsylvania PA
California CA	Michigan MI	Puerto Rico PR
Colorado CO	Minnesota MN	Rhode Island RI
Connecticut CT	Mississippi MS	South Carolina SC
Delaware DE	Missouri MO	South Dakota SD
District of Columbia DC	Montana MT	Tennesse TN
Florida FL	Nebraska NE	Texas TX
Georgia GA	Nevada NV	Utah UT
Hawaii HI	New Hampshire NH	Vermont VT
Idaho ID	New Jersey NJ	Virginia VA
Illinois IL	New Mexico NM	Washington WA
Indiana IN	New York NY	West Virginia WV
Iowa IA	North Carolina NC	Wisconsin WI
Kansas KS	North Dakota ND	Wyoming WY
Kentucky KY		

Objects, direct, *see* Direct objects
Opinions, used to develop paragraph, 238
Outline form, 255

Paragraphs
coherence in, 241
defined, 231–32
descriptive, 247–48
details, reasons, examples in, 237–38, 241, 243, 249
developing main idea in, 237–38
expository, 249–50
narrative, 245–46
narrowing topic of, 235
notes for, 253
order of importance in, 242
organization of, 241–42
outline for, 241
planning, 253
repetition in, 244
selecting a topic for, 251
space order, 242
subject for, 235
time order in, 241
topic sentence in, 233, 235, 237–38, 241, 243, 248, 249
transitions in, 243
tying ideas together in, 243
unity in, 231
Parenthetical expressions, commas for, 91
Participle
past, 187, 189, 191
present, 187
Parts of speech, determined by use, 18
Past participle, 187, 189, 191
Past tense, 187, 189, 191
peace, piece, 185
Periods
inside quotation marks, 99
statements followed by, 87, 121
Personal pronouns, 149, 150, 151, 167
Phrase fragments, 117
Phrases
adjective, 15
adverb, 15
defined, 117
prepositional, 13, 15, 31, 71, 171
plain, plane, 185
Plot of story, 253
Plural nouns, 95, 167
Plural pronouns, 167, 175
Plural verbs, 169, 170, 173, 175, 177
Point of view in composition, 251–52
Predicates
complete, 27
defined, 26
verbs in, 27
Prefixes, 67, 83
Prepositional phrases
adjective and adverb, 15
between subject and verb, 171
combining sentences with, 215
defined, 13
distinguished from clause, 71
never containing direct object, 31
Prepositions
defined, 13
object of, 155
Present participle, 187
Present tense, 187, 189, 191

Principal parts of verbs, 187
Pronouns
blunders in use of, 157
defined, 3
indefinite, 175
object, 149, 153, 155
personal, 149, 150, 151, 167
plural, 167, 175
after prepositions, 155
relative, 53, 55, 57, 61
singular, 167, 175
subject, 149–50
subject complements, as, 151
subject-verb agreement and, 169, 170, 175
Proper adjectives, 137
Proper nouns, 1, 133, 135, 137
Punctuation, *see* specific marks

Question marks, 87, 99, 121
quiet, quite, 205
Quotation marks, 99, 101
Quotations
direct, 99
indirect, 99
punctuation of, 99, 101

Relative pronouns, 53, 55, 57, 61
Repetition, use of, 244
Request letter, 275
Rewriting composition, 257
Run-on sentences, 113, 121, 131

said, synonyms for, 264
Salutation
of business letter, 273, 274
of social letter, 269, 270
Sentence bases, 29–30
Sentence combining
with adjectives, adverbs, 211
with adjective clauses, 221, 223
with adverb clauses, 225
with compound subjects, compound verbs, 217
with independent clauses, 219
Sentence fragments, 113, 115, 117
Sentences
beginning with *here, there, where,* 173
compound, 41, 51, 77
defined, 25
imperative, 87
predicate of, 26
run-on, 113, 121
simple, 41, 51, 77
subject of, 26
topic, 233, 235, 237–38, 241, 243, 248, 249
transitional, 243–44
turned-about, 173
set, sit, use of, 193
Signature
in business letter, 273, 274
in social letter, 269, 270
Simple sentences, 41, 51, 77
Simple subjects, 27
Singular nouns, 95, 167
Singular pronouns, 167, 175
Singular verbs, 169, 173, 177
sit, set, use of, 193
Social letters, 269–70, 271–72
soul, sole, 185
Spelling
articulation and, 165

doubling final consonant, 131, 147
final *e* plus suffix, 85
final *y* plus suffix, 107
homophones, 185
long vowels, 49
short vowels, 23
the sound /f/, 69
sounds and, 23, 49, 165, 205–06
words often confused, 205
Storytelling, 263–64
Subject complements, 33, 151, 153
Subjects
agreement in number with verbs, 167, 169, 170, 171, 173, 175, 177
complete, 27
compound, 39, 157, 177
defined, 26
duplicate, 157
pronouns as, 149
simple, 27
Subordinate clauses
adjective, 53
adverb, 71
combining sentences, 221, 223, 225
defined, 51–52
distinguished from sentence, 115
Subordinating conjunctions, 73, 115
Suffixes, 105, 107, 147
Suspense, in story, 263
Synonyms
defined, 145
for *said,* 264
one-word definition, 163

take, bring, use of, 197
Tenses, 187, 189, 191
Thank-you note, 272
that, which, clauses beginning with, 57
there, their, they're, 185
Three-part sentence base, 29–30
threw, through, use of, 206
Titles, capitals for, 139–40
to, too, 205
Topic sentences, 233, 235, 237–38, 241, 243, 248, 249
Transitions in paragraph, 243–44
Two-part sentence base, 29

Verbs
action, 7, 9, 31, 35
agreement in number with subjects, 167, 169, 170, 171, 173, 175, 177
compound, 39
defined, 7
helping, 7, 189, 191
irregular, 187, 189, 191
linking, 9, 33, 35, 151
plural, agreement of subjects with, 169, 170, 173, 177
in predicates, 27
principal parts of, 187
singular, agreement of subjects with, 169, 170, 173, 177
subjects and, 27
tenses of, 187, 189, 191

waist, waste, 185
well, good, use of, 36
which, that, clauses beginning with, 57
whose, who's, 185
who, whom, whose, clauses beginning with, 55
Word picture, 261–62

INDEX OF VOCABULARY WORDS
(Page numbers refer to definitions in text)

A NOTE ON SPELLING

Writing may be thought of as a way of recording the sounds of speech by the use of symbols that represent those sounds. The letters in our alphabet are the symbols we use to represent our speech sounds. If we had a different letter for each sound, spelling would be easy; just a matter of knowing which letter to use for each sound. Unfortunately, English spelling is not that simple. There are more sounds than there are letters in the alphabet to represent them, and so the task of learning to spell in our language is somewhat complicated.

The complications, however, may be partially overcome by becoming aware of, and learning, the many *spelling patterns* that do exist. These patterns involve the use of various combinations of letters to spell certain sounds.

To show the *sounds* of a word, rather than the letters, a special phonetic alphabet has been developed. Using this phonetic alphabet will help you understand the relationship between sounds and letters, and thereby help you to become a better speller.

On the next two pages are two charts. The first one, entitled "Consonant Sounds and Their Common Spellings," summarizes twenty-four main consonant sounds of English, the symbols used to represent these sounds, and common ways of spelling them. The *symbol* for each consonant sound is written between a pair of slanted lines. For example, the symbol /k/ stands for the sound of the first letter in the word *kit,* as you can see by looking at the chart. The sound /k/ may also be spelled by the letters *c* (as in *cold*), *ck* (as in *lick*), or *ke* (as in *like*).

The second chart, "Vowel Sounds and Their Common Spellings," shows the symbols for fourteen main vowel sounds, and the vowel sound called a *schwa*. If you look at the vowel sound /ī/ on the chart, you will see the several patterns or ways in which this sound may be spelled. For example, in the word *line*, it is spelled with the letter *i* followed by a consonant (*n*), which, in turn, is followed by an *e*. (The letters **VCe**, standing for *vowel, consonant, e,* represent *one* of the ways or patterns in which the sound /ī/ may be written in English.) Other ways include *–igh* as in *high; –y* as in *try; –ie* as in *die*.

The spelling patterns reflected in these two charts should help to balance the irregularities of English spelling. The point is, that *despite* exceptions and seemingly illogical spellings, our spelling system exists as it does for good historical reasons, and is, on the whole, a predictable system.

Consonant Sounds and Their Common Spellings

Sound	At the Beginning	At the End
/p/	**p:** pie	**p:** rip; **pe:** ripe
/t/	**t:** ten	**t:** pet; **te:** date
/k/	**k:** kit; **c:** cold	**ck:** lick; **ke:** like
/ch/	**ch:** chin	**tch:** witch; **ch:** reach
/b/	**b:** bed	**b:** tub; **be:** tube
/d/	**d:** do	**d:** rid; **de:** ride
/g/	**g:** get	**g:** beg; **gue:** league
/j/	**j:** jet; **g:** gentle	**dge:** budge; **ge:** cage
/f/	**f:** fun; **ph:** phrase	**ff:** stuff; **fe:** life; **f:** beef; **ph:** paragraph
/v/	**v:** very	**ve:** save
/s/	**s:** see; **c:** center	**ss:** glass; **s:** bus; **se:** case; **ce:** rice
/z/	**z:** zoo	**z:** quiz; **zz:** buzz; **se:** rose; **ze:** sneeze
/sh/	**sh:** ship	**sh:** push
/zh/	**j:** Jacques	**ge:** rouge; (in the middle) **s:** treasure
/r/	**r:** run; **wr:** wrist; **rh:** rhyme	**r:** car; **re:** care
/l/	**l:** lose	**ll:** pill; **le:** smile; **l:** fail
/m/	**m:** move	**m:** Sam; **me:** same; **mb:** tomb
/n/	**n:** nose; **gn:** gnaw; **kn:** know	**n:** pin; **ne:** pine
/ng/		**ng:** strong; **n:** trunk
/th/	**th:** thick	**th:** path
/t̶h̶/	**th:** then	**th:** smooth; **the:** bathe
/y/	**y:** you; **u** /yū/: use	
/w/	**w:** will; **o** /wu/: one; **qu** /kw/: quick	
/h/	**h:** hat; **wh:** who	

© 1982 HBJ

Key to English Grammar and Composition

The following chart correlates lessons in *English Workshop, Second Course* to the appropriate rule in *English Grammar and Composition, Second Course*.

Workshop Lesson	Text Rule	Workshop Lesson	Text Rule
1	2a	67	12d
2	2b	68	12f
3	2c	69	12g
4–5	3a	72	23b
6	3b	73	26d–i
7	3c	74	10a–b
8	4a–d	75	10a–b
9	3d–f	76	10c–d
11	23b,25a,25c	77	10c–d
15	6a	83	8a
16	6b	84	8b,8m
17	6d	85	8c
18	11a	86	8l
21	7a–b,13h	87	8d–f
24	23b	88	8g–i
26	5a–c	93	9a–b
27–31	5d	94–98	9c
34	23b,25d	101	25f
36–39	5e	103	16a
43	26d–i	104	16a
44	13a–d	105	16c–e
45	13f–g,13i–j	106	16f
46	13k–l	107	16f
47	13m	108	16f
48	14q–r	111	19a,19g
49	14s	112	19b
50	14g–h,14j–l	113	19c
51	14i,14m–n	114	19d,19f
54	25e	115	19h
55	26d–i	116	19i
56	15a	120	20a–c,21b
57	15b	121	20d–e,21d–f
58	4a,15c	122	20h
60	15e	126	21g
64	25f	127	22a–d
65	26d–i	128	22e–f
66	12d,12e		

B 2
C 3
D 4
E 5
F 6
G 7
H 8
I 9
J 0

Key to *English Grammar and Composition*

The following chart correlates lessons in *English Workshop, Second Course* to the appropriate rule in *English Grammar and Composition, Second Course.*

Workshop Lesson	Text Rule	Workshop Lesson	Text Rule
1	2a	67	12d
2	2b	68	12f
3	2c	69	12g
4–5	3a	72	23b
6	3b	73	26d–i
7	3c	74	10a–b
8	4a–d	75	10a–b
9	3d–f	76	10c–d
11	23b,25a,25c	77	10c–d
15	6a	83	8a
16	6b	84	8b,8m
17	6d	85	8c
18	11a	86	8l
21	7a–b,13h	87	8d–f
24	23b	88	8g–i
26	5a–c	93	9a–b
27–31	5d	94–98	9c
34	23b,25d	101	25f
36–39	5e	103	16a
43	26d–i	104	16a
44	13a–d	105	16c–e
45	13f–g,13i–j	106	16f
46	13k–l	107	16f
47	13m	108	16f
48	14q–r	111	19a,19g
49	14s	112	19b
50	14g–h,14j–l	113	19c
51	14i,14m–n	114	19d,19f
54	25e	115	19h
55	26d–i	116	19i
56	15a	120	20a–c,21b
57	15b	121	20d–e,21d–f
58	4a,15c	122	20h
60	15e	126	21g
64	25f	127	22a–d
65	26d–i	128	22e–f
66	12d,12e		

Vowel Sounds and Their Common Spellings

Fourteen Vowel Sounds

Sounds	/i/	/e/	/a/	/u/	/o/
Spellings and Examples	i: hit	e: red ea: dead	a: cat	u: but o: son	o: top a: far

Sounds	/ī/	/ē/	/ā/	/ū/	/ō/
Spellings and Examples	VCe: line igh: high y: try ie: die	VCe: Pete ee: deed ea: heat e: he ie: chief ei: deceive	VCe: lame ai: wait ay: pay ei: weigh	VCe: June oo: root ew: few ue: Sue o: to	VCe: lone oa: goat ow: slow oe: hoe o: no

Sounds	/o͞o/	/ou/	/oi/	/au/
Spellings and Examples	oo: look u: push	ou: out ow: cow	oi: oil oy: toy	au: haul aw: flaw a: ball o: long ough: fought augh: caught

The Vowel Sound Schwa /ə/

	i	e	ea	u	o
In Words of One Syllable	stir girl	were her	learn earth	burn spur	world worse

	-er	-or	-ar			
The Sound /ər/	runner maker father	actor orator navigator	beggar liar sugar			

	-al	-le	-el	-ul	-ile	-il
The Sound /əl/	legal moral rural	steeple battle circle	camel satchel travel	beautiful useful helpful	fertile juvenile hostile	April evil council

	-en	-an	-ain	-in		
The Sound /ən/	frozen deepen oaken garden	American orphan woman organ	captain curtain mountain certain	robin cabin basin cousin		